MACMILLAN / McGRAW-HILL

Teacher's READ-ALOUD ANTHOLOGY

Margaret H. Lippert

Anthologist

*As part of Macmillan / McGraw-Hill's effort to help make a
difference to the environment, this anthology has been printed on recycled paper.*

MACMILLAN / McGRAW-HILL SCHOOL PUBLISHING COMPANY

New York • Chicago • Columbus

The cover illustration, by Kent Barton, depicts an African storyteller who is sharing his story with a group of children in a museum auditorium. The performer adds power to his story by beating an African drum.

1995 Printing

Macmillan/McGraw-Hill School Division
10 Union Square East
New York, New York 10003

Printed in the United States of America

ISBN 0-02-179120-1 / 3

3 4 5 6 7 8 9   DBH   99 98 97 96 95 94

This book is dedicated to
you, the teacher, who will pick
the words of these stories up
off the page and send them
into the hearts and minds of
your students, and to you,
the listeners, who will take
the words and build them
into images.

MARGARET H. LIPPERT

ᴀcknowledgments

The publisher gratefully acknowledges permission to reprint the following copyrighted material:

Atheneum Publishers
"Jackal's Favorite Game" from LION AND THE OSTRICH CHICKS AND OTHER AF-RICAN FOLK TALES by Ashley Bryan. Copyright © 1986 by Ashley Bryan. Reprinted with permission of Atheneum Publishers, an imprint of Macmillan Publishing Company.

Byrd Baylor
"The Maze" from AND IT IS STILL THAT WAY: *Legends told by Arizona Indian Children with Notes by Byrd Baylor.* Copyright © 1976 by Byrd Baylor. Published by Trails West Press, Santa Fe, New Mexico. Reprinted by permission of Byrd Baylor.

Pura Belpré
"The Shepherd and the Princess" from THE TIGER AND THE RABBIT AND OTHER TALES by Pura Belpré. Copyright © 1944, 1946, 1963 by Pura Belpré. Reprinted by permission of the author.

The Caxton Printers, Ltd.
"When the Rain Came Up from China" from TALL TIMBER TALES by Dell J. McCormick. Copyright © 1986 by The Caxton Printers, Ltd. Published by The Caxton Printers, Ltd., Caldwell, Idaho 83605. Reprinted by permission of the publisher.

E.P. Dutton
THE GUNNIWOLF by Wilhelmina Harper. Copyright © 1918, 1946 by Wilhelmina Harper. Used by permission of Dutton Children's Books, a division of Penguin Books USA Inc.

Floating Eaglefeather
"Why the Baby Says, 'Goo-Goo' " from . . . AND THE EARTH LIVED HAPPILY EVER AFTER . . . OLD AND NEW TRADITIONAL TALES TO WAGE PEACE, by Floating Eaglefeather. Copyright © 1987 by Floating Eaglefeather. Reprinted with permission of Floating Eaglefeather AKA: Samy E. Weinberger of New Orleans, Louisiana.

HarperCollins Publishers
Excerpts from CHARLOTTE'S WEB by E.B. White (Text Chapters 1-3, pp. 1-24). Copyright 1952 by E.B. White. Renewed © 1980 by E.B. White. Selection reprinted by permission of HarperCollins Publishers.

"Spider's Friends and Foes" and "Father Spider Comes to Dinner" from SOMEONE SAW A SPIDER by Shirley Climo. Text Copyright © 1985 by Shirley Climo. Reprinted by permission of HarperCollins Publishers.

Ken Jackson (Grey Eagle)
"How Wolf Helped the Sami" by Ken Jackson (Grey Eagle). Copyright © 1991 by Ken Jackson (Grey Eagle). Used with permission of the author.

Cover Illustration: Kent Barton

Cover Design: Circa 86, Inc.

Illustration Credits: Fian Arroyo, 31, 87-89; Alex Bloch, 99-105; Jean Cassels, 16, 17; Circa 86, Inc., 22-29, 37, 38, 49-60; Susan Dodge, 18-21; Grace Goldberg, 92-94; Carol Greger, 32-34, 41, 42; Janet Hamlin, 61, 62; Liz Kenyon, 90, 91; Lingta Kung, 39, 40; Kelly Maddox, 35, 36; John Murray, 73-79; Cathy O'Connor, 71, 72; Vilma Oritz, 43-48; Nisa Rauschenberg, 63-70; Scott Sawyer, 30; Susan Swan, 80, 81; Jean and Mou-Sien Tseng, 82-86; Yemi, 95-98, 106-110.

CONTENTS

INTRODUCTION

by Margaret H. Lippert

Long before I wrote stories, I listened for stories. Listening for them is something more acute than listening to them. I suppose it's an early form of participation in what goes on. Listening children know stories are there. When their elders sit and begin, children are just waiting and hoping for one to come out, like a mouse from its hole.

EUDORA WELTY[1]

This book is stuffed with mice. Your students are waiting.

You are part of a long tradition of storytellers and story readers. Stories belong to us all. From ancient times, people have been entertained and nourished by stories. All of us in our own families and culture have, like Eudora Welty, been entranced by the tales that have been told to us from the time we first started to listen. From these stories, we learned about listening and speaking and then about reading—connecting the images and messages of stories with print and with books.

The power of stories draws us to ideas and thoughts and feelings that we want and need to explore. Through stories we learn about the experiences of others and come to understand ourselves better. The best stories take us from where we are and lead us, word by word, image by image, into places known and unknown, familiar and new, comfortable and exciting.

Reading aloud opens students to a new way of learning—listening. Many of us, and many of our students, are unaccustomed to listening carefully. We tune out much of what goes on around us. We need to remember the power of listening and help our students do the same.

Reading aloud can grip students in a listening vise—because they want to know what will happen next, they listen with fully focused attention. Since students can understand a much larger vocabulary than they can read themselves, when we read aloud we expose them to more sophisticated concepts and content than they could read independently. People of traditional cultures knew this—they passed on knowledge through their stories.

As you read aloud, you give your students stories and something of yourself. You build a community in your classroom that links you and your students to one another, to the story, and to the thinking and feeling of the author and the culture from which that story springs. Your students stretch and grow, discovering the pathways and journeys of others and, in the process, making discoveries of their own.

A READ-ALOUD CELEBRATION

Each Read Aloud in this collection relates in some way—theme, style, author, content—to a selection in the Macmillan/McGraw-Hill Reading/Language Arts student anthologies. Many of the Read Alouds are traditional tales, stories that were handed down from one generation to another within a particular culture. Traditional stories include folk tales, fairy tales, myths, legends, tall tales, and fables. In addition to traditional literature, classics and contemporary literature are represented.

In order to root this collection in the traditional oral heritage from which stories spring, I interviewed people who grew up in storytelling cultures and taped them telling stories so that you and your students would have access to their wisdom and to their stories. Some of these gifted storytellers are included on the SONGS AND STORIES AUDIOCASSETTES that are offered with the series.

The information about the contributors and the indexes at the end of the collection provide important information for you to share with your students about the origins of the tales and of the tellers.

HINTS FOR EFFECTIVE READING ALOUD

It is preferable, though not absolutely necessary, to skim through a story before you read it aloud. That way you will know where the story is headed, and you can adjust your reading style to the mood and rhythm of the story.

As you read, take your time and read with involvement and intensity. Your students will need time to construct story images and to process ideas as the story moves along. To help you judge the time you will need to allow for each story reading, the range of times it took several different teachers to read each story aloud to a group of students is included in the CONTENTS.

Sometimes questions will arise in response to a story. When this happens, I often ask students if they can answer the questions that have been raised. I have done this countless times, and, no matter how difficult the question, no student has ever said, "I don't know." Within the story's context, they do know, and they help one another explore the answers to their own questions.

Now I often ask after reading or telling a story, "Was there any part of the story that was unclear to you?" or "What did you wonder about as you listened to the story?" There are always many questions. And frequently there are many answers to a question. The harder the question, the more ideas and responses the question seems to generate. For example, after hearing me tell *Yeh-Shen*,[2] which is a Chinese version of the Cinderella story, one third grader asked, "Why did the stepmother kill the fish?" Seven children offered seven different explanations. Some of the responses were as follows: "Maybe she didn't like the fish." "One of the reasons could be that she wanted the meat from the fish. Or that she didn't want the girl [Yeh-Shen] to be friends with the fish." "I think she was just plain mean."

The students listened to the story. They struggled with parts that were unclear or unexplained, and they integrated all of their previous knowledge with the information generated in the story. They also developed plausible explanations to justify the actions of the characters and the events in the story.

In an atmosphere where questions are encouraged, hard questions are more likely to rise to the surface so they can be explored. Every question is a new starting point. Through ALL their questions, students seek meaning and struggle collaboratively to find answers to their own puzzling questions about the stories. What a wonderful model for seeking responses to the puzzling questions that confront them in their lives.

"I DO AND I UNDERSTAND"

There is an ancient Chinese proverb: "I hear and I forget. I see and I remember. I do and I understand."

By reading these stories aloud, you make them part of the oral tradition. Just listening to these stories will enrich the imaginations of your students, offering them new ideas and insights. But if your students re-create a favorite story in another form, it will become theirs in an even deeper way. "Doing" the stories leads to further understanding and appreciation of them.

Your students may wish to retell the story as a group in their own words, or to illustrate or depict the story in paintings, collages, or dioramas. They may enjoy spontaneously reenacting the story without props or scenery, or perhaps with the simplest of these. They may choose to write their favorite or least favorite part of the story, or their own version of the story either in whole or in part. If they do any of these things, either prompted by you or motivated on their own, they will know the story more intimately. The better they know the story, the more comfortable they will feel with it, and the better they will like it. The more they like it, the more they will want to share it, perhaps even outside the classroom, with family or friends. Thus the oral tradition continues.

ONWARD TO STORYTELLING

As a storyteller and story lover, I would be remiss if I did not encourage you to try telling, without the text, a tale or two. Telling a story is fun. It also models for students the possibility that they, too, can recall, retell, and enjoy stories whenever they wish. If you've told stories before, you know the flexibility and closeness engendered by direct contact with listeners, without an intervening page. If you haven't, you could begin with a short, familiar tale.

You don't need to memorize the words to enjoy telling stories. In fact, memorizing the words may distract you from the images and sequence of the tale itself. I simply picture the story as it takes place, then describe it to my listeners as I "see" it. This is the same skill you use when relating an anecdote that happened to you or when telling a joke. As a teacher, you already know how to hold the attention of your class. Storytelling is one small step beyond explaining a concept or describing an assignment.

The author-storyteller-artist Ashley Bryan has a favorite African proverb: "He who learns, teaches!" Learn the craft of storytelling along with your students. Allow them to watch you struggle and try and learn. Make mistakes and work through your mistakes. Allow them also to watch you as you succeed and soar on the wings of new stories. This will teach them about your love of story and language, and about how much you are willing to risk for them.

ENDINGS AND BEGINNINGS

From here, it is up to you. The stories are yours now. Read them, enjoy them, pass them along. By sharing these stories with your students, you will preserve them for at least one more generation.

Since this is a book of stories, I'd like to end this introduction with a story, or to be more accurate, a part of a Russian folk tale that is my favorite story. The oldest man in the village, encouraging a young boy to tell his first story to the expectant listeners around the fire, says:

A story is a letter that comes to us from yesterday. Each person who tells it adds his word to the message and sends it on to tomorrow. So begin.

from "The Tale of the Tales"[3]

[1] Eudora Welty, *One Writer's Beginnings* (Cambridge, MA: Harvard University Press, 1983), p. 16.

[2] Ai-Ling Louie, *Yeh-Shen: A Cinderella Story from China* (New York: Philomel Books, 1982).

[3] George and Helen Papashvily, "The Tale of the Tales," *Yes and No Stories: A Book of Georgian Folk Tales* (New York: Harper & Brothers, 1946).

I can promise that once you begin the daily experience of reading aloud to children, it will become one of the best parts of your day and the children's day, minutes and hours that will be treasured for years to come.

JIM TRELEASE
from *The Read-Aloud Handbook*

15

THE CLEVER TURTLE

a folk tale from Brazil retold by Margaret H. Lippert

Wheet-weedle-whoo, wheet-weedle-whoo, wheet-wheet-wheet-whoo. Every day, Turtle sat by the Amazon River and played her flute. All the birds and animals loved to listen to her play.

One day, a man walking through the forest heard her beautiful music. Wheet-weedle-whoo, wheet-weedle-whoo, wheet-wheet-wheet-whoo.

He stopped to listen. When he saw that a turtle was playing the flute, he thought about dinner.

"Turtle soup would be a treat tonight," he thought. So he picked Turtle up and carried her home.

He put Turtle into a cage made of branches and closed the lid. "Don't let the turtle out of the cage," he said to his children. "Tonight we will have turtle soup." Then the father picked up his hoe and went to work in the garden. The children played in the yard.

Turtle did not want to be made into soup. She started to play her flute. Wheet-weedle-whoo, wheet-weedle-whoo, wheet-wheet-wheet-whoo. The children stopped their game and listened.

"Turtle is playing the flute!" they shouted.

"I can dance as well as I can play," called Turtle. "I can even play and dance at the same time. If you open the lid you can watch me." The children opened the lid, and Turtle started to dance.

Wheet-weedle-whoo. Crash-bam. Wheet-weedle-whoo. Crash-bam. Turtle's shell banged against the sides of the cage as she danced.

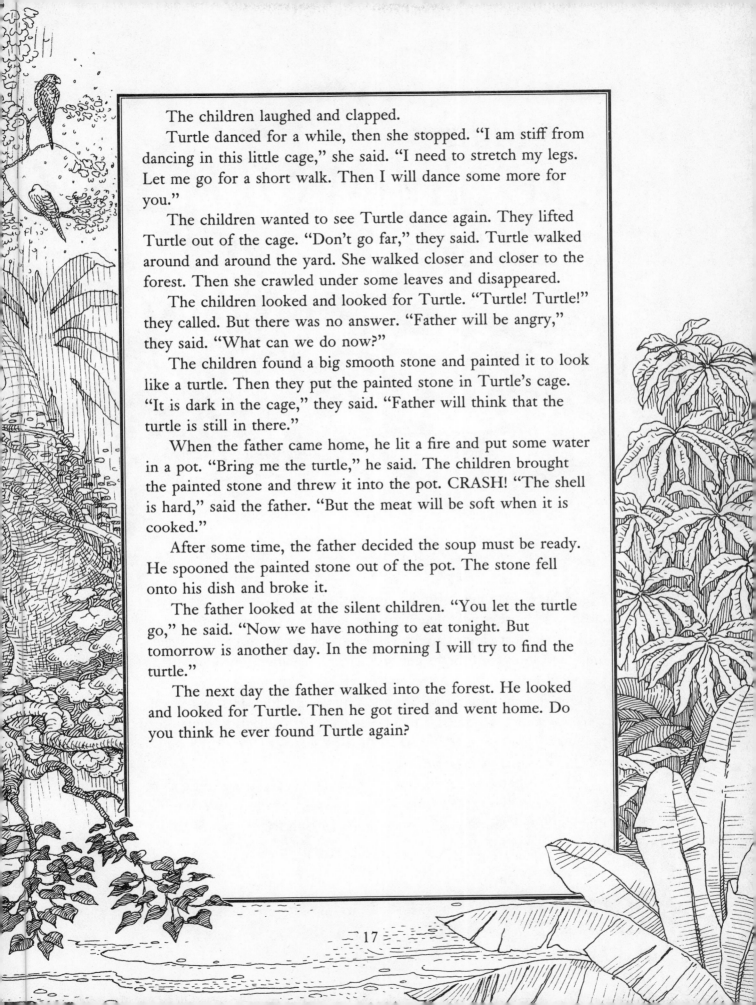

The children laughed and clapped.

Turtle danced for a while, then she stopped. "I am stiff from dancing in this little cage," she said. "I need to stretch my legs. Let me go for a short walk. Then I will dance some more for you."

The children wanted to see Turtle dance again. They lifted Turtle out of the cage. "Don't go far," they said. Turtle walked around and around the yard. She walked closer and closer to the forest. Then she crawled under some leaves and disappeared.

The children looked and looked for Turtle. "Turtle! Turtle!" they called. But there was no answer. "Father will be angry," they said. "What can we do now?"

The children found a big smooth stone and painted it to look like a turtle. Then they put the painted stone in Turtle's cage. "It is dark in the cage," they said. "Father will think that the turtle is still in there."

When the father came home, he lit a fire and put some water in a pot. "Bring me the turtle," he said. The children brought the painted stone and threw it into the pot. CRASH! "The shell is hard," said the father. "But the meat will be soft when it is cooked."

After some time, the father decided the soup must be ready. He spooned the painted stone out of the pot. The stone fell onto his dish and broke it.

The father looked at the silent children. "You let the turtle go," he said. "Now we have nothing to eat tonight. But tomorrow is another day. In the morning I will try to find the turtle."

The next day the father walked into the forest. He looked and looked for Turtle. Then he got tired and went home. Do you think he ever found Turtle again?

THE GUNNIWOLF

an American folk tale retold
by Wilhelmina Harper

There was once a little girl who lived with her mother very close to a dense jungle. Each day the mother would caution Little Girl to be most careful and never enter the jungle, because—if she did—the Gunniwolf might get her! Little Girl always promised that she would never, NEVER even go NEAR the jungle.

One day the mother had to go away for a while. Her last words were to caution Little Girl that whatever else she did she must keep far away from the jungle! And Little Girl was very sure that she would not go anywhere *near* it.

The mother was hardly out of sight, however, when Little Girl noticed some beautiful white flowers growing at the very edge of the jungle. "Oh," she thought, "wouldn't I love to have some of those—I'll pick just a few."

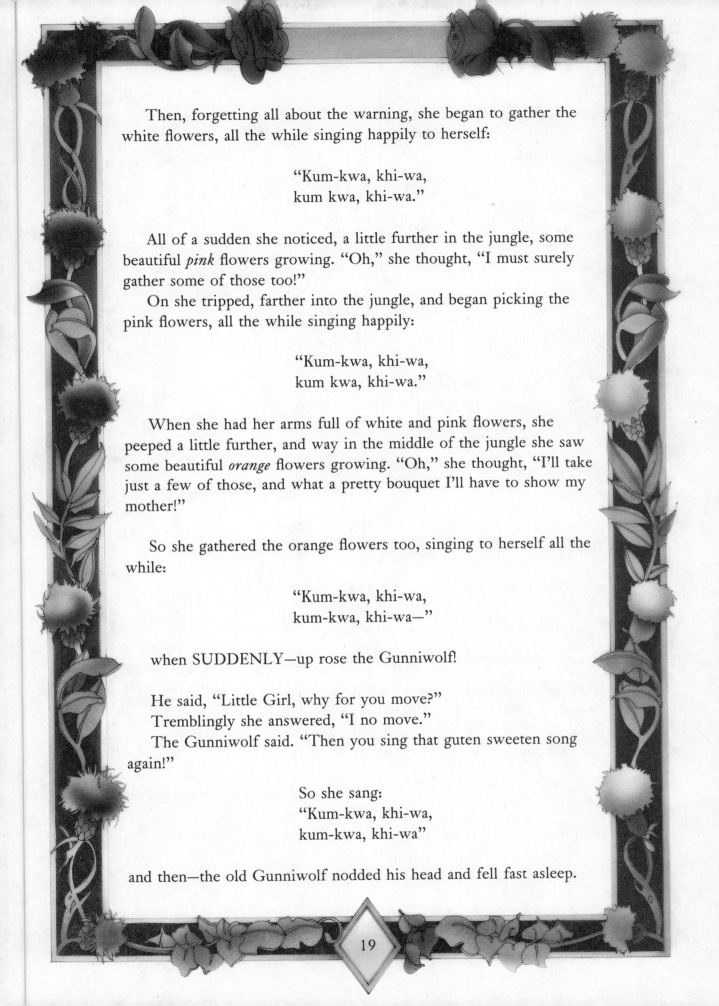

Then, forgetting all about the warning, she began to gather the white flowers, all the while singing happily to herself:

> "Kum-kwa, khi-wa,
> kum kwa, khi-wa."

All of a sudden she noticed, a little further in the jungle, some beautiful *pink* flowers growing. "Oh," she thought, "I must surely gather some of those too!"

On she tripped, farther into the jungle, and began picking the pink flowers, all the while singing happily:

> "Kum-kwa, khi-wa,
> kum kwa, khi-wa."

When she had her arms full of white and pink flowers, she peeped a little further, and way in the middle of the jungle she saw some beautiful *orange* flowers growing. "Oh," she thought, "I'll take just a few of those, and what a pretty bouquet I'll have to show my mother!"

So she gathered the orange flowers too, singing to herself all the while:

> "Kum-kwa, khi-wa,
> kum-kwa, khi-wa—"

when SUDDENLY—up rose the Gunniwolf!

He said, "Little Girl, why for you move?"
Tremblingly she answered, "I no move."
The Gunniwolf said. "Then you sing that guten sweeten song again!"

> So she sang:
> "Kum-kwa, khi-wa,
> kum-kwa, khi-wa"

and then—the old Gunniwolf nodded his head and fell fast asleep.

Away ran Little Girl as fast as ever she could:

    pit-pat.   pit-pat.   pit-pat.
         pit-pat.   pit-pat.

Then the Gunniwolf woke up! Away he ran:

    hunker-cha,
                  hunker-cha,
                          hunker-cha

until he caught up to her. And he said, "Little Girl, why for you move?"

"I no move," she answered.
"Then you sing that guten, sweeten song again!"
Timidly she sang:

        "Kum-kwa, khi-wa,
        kum-kwa, khi-wa."

Then the old Gunniwolf nodded, nodded, and went sound asleep.

Away ran Little Girl just as fast as ever she could:

    pit-pat,   pit-pat,   pit-pat—
         pit-pat,   pit-pat,

and again the Gunniwolf woke up! Away he ran:
hunker-cha, hunker-cha, hunker-cha, hunker-cha—

    pit-pat.   pit-pat—
         pit-pat.

                            hunker-cha, hunker-cha—

until he caught up to her and said, "Little Girl, why for you move?"
    "I no move."

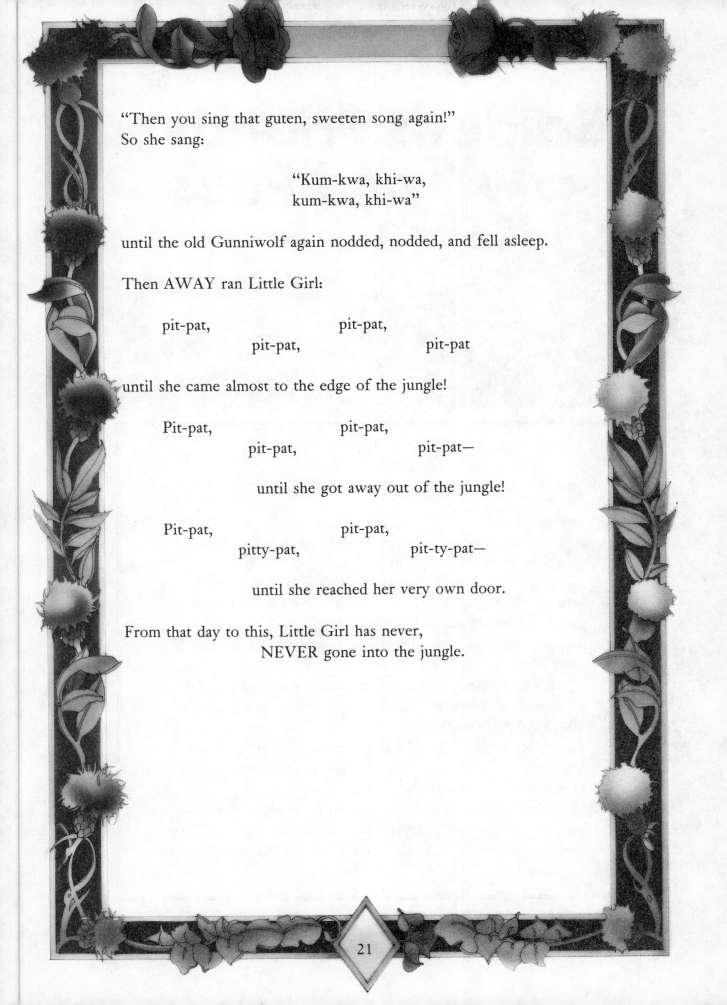

"Then you sing that guten, sweeten song again!"
So she sang:

> "Kum-kwa, khi-wa,
> kum-kwa, khi-wa"

until the old Gunniwolf again nodded, nodded, and fell asleep.

Then AWAY ran Little Girl:

    pit-pat,   pit-pat,
        pit-pat,   pit-pat

until she came almost to the edge of the jungle!

    Pit-pat,   pit-pat,
        pit-pat,   pit-pat—

        until she got away out of the jungle!

    Pit-pat,   pit-pat,
        pitty-pat,   pit-ty-pat—

        until she reached her very own door.

From that day to this, Little Girl has never,
             NEVER gone into the jungle.

Spider's Friends and Foes

a nonfiction selection by Shirley Climo

Why did the fly fly?
Because the spider spied her.

Scientists say it is likely that, millions of years ago, insects first developed wings to get away from spiders. But it is a good thing for us that a great many of them don't escape too easily.

Spiders eat more pests than birds, and they do the job more safely than pesticides. Without spiders, the earth would be a pretty unpleasant place. We would be up to our knees in bugs and our stomachs would be empty, for insects would devour most of the food.

In England and Wales, it is estimated that spiders catch at least two hundred trillion insects every year. That's 200,000,000,000,000. If you could put those bugs in a bag and place them on one side of a giant scale and then squeeze all the human beings in England onto the other, the insects that spiders caught would outweigh the people.

Although spiders are their own worst enemies (for spiders prey on one another), they are among our best friends. That is the fact behind this folk tale from Russia, "Father Spider Comes to Dinner."

FATHER SPIDER COMES TO DINNER

a Russian folk tale retold by Shirley Climo

Summers on the steppes of Russia are usually dry. But one year, in the time of the Tsars, rain fell in June, throughout July, and again in August. The dogs and cats—especially the cats—hated the daily drizzles. But the horses and cows were happy, for the grass grew high and they could graze to their stomachs' content. The old men and women complained about the dampness, but the frogs and the children—especially the children—were delighted, for there were dozens of mud puddles to jump over and in.

The mosquitoes and the gnats, the midges and the mites, the flies and the fleas, liked this summer best of all. The wetter the weather, the better for them. Like the grass, they kept growing, both in size and numbers.

After a while the animals, and the people, whatever their ages, were miserable. Everyone itched and scratched. At night, the humming of the mosquitoes was louder than thunder in their ears. By day, flies the size of turnips tracked mud on the ceilings and knocked saucepans from stove tops. Fleas were as big as bumblebees.

One village was so plagued that on an August morning, when the clock in the square struck nine, the town magistrate called everyone together. "Nothing's to be done about the weather," said he, "but something must be done about these buzzing, biting pests."

The villagers were too busy swatting and slapping to answer. Most dared not open their mouths for fear of swallowing a fly. Then one woman, so old and shriveled that even insects found her too dry for their tastes, spoke up.

"When I was a girl, my great-granny talked of a strange animal called Father Spider who lives in the forest beyond the steppes. She said none could match him at gnat catching."

"Ah!" cried the magistrate. "Then we will invite this spider to come and catch as many of the creepers, the crawlers, the biters, and the buzzers as he pleases." He looked around the square. "Who will go into the forest to find Father Spider?"

In the center of the square by the well, a lad named Ivan raised his hand to swat at the mosquito that circled round his head.

"Splendid!" The magistrate smiled. "Brave Ivan has volunteered!"

At once, Ivan was bundled from head to toe in woolen wrappings to protect him from the insects. His mother kissed the tip of his nose, which was all that showed, and rubbed it with pitch from a pine tree so that no bug would be tempted to nip it.

"Now be off," ordered the magistrate, but not unkindly.

"And be home before dark," added his mother.

Ivan had taken only a half dozen steps when he turned back to the square.

"Please," he asked in a voice muffled by the scarf tied over his chin, "how will I know the spider when I meet him?"

No one answered, for none of the villagers had ever seen a spider. Finally the old woman spoke again.

"My great-granny told me that Father Spider could spin." She held up her distaff wound with wool.

Ivan nodded as best he was able and marched down the slippery cobbled street and up the muddy, puddled road. When he reached the woods, he stopped and filled his pockets with pebbles. He scattered them as he went so as to be sure of finding his way home again.

The forest was gloomy, with a musty, mossy smell, and alive with snaps and crackles as creatures scurried away at his approach. Ivan counted fox and marten and deer and skipped a pebble at a hare. He saw the paw prints of bears by his feet, and birds of every feather squawked over his head. But none of these animals could spin, and none looked likely to learn.

As Ivan dropped pebble after pebble, his pockets got lighter and he walked faster. He could not tell how far he'd come, nor even the time of day, for the tall trees hid the sun. His woolen wraps were hot and scratchy and Ivan's backbone tickled. He was certain a bug or two had been bundled beneath the layers. Then, quite clear and close, he heard the howl of a wolf.

Ivan emptied out his pockets and began to run. One direction was as good as another so long as it was away from the voice of the wolf. As he ran, something stuck to the pitch on the end of his nose. Ivan brushed at it impatiently with a mittened hand.

"Clumsy!" someone scolded. "You've torn my net!"

Dangling above Ivan, almost touching the tassel on his cap, was the queerest animal Ivan had ever laid eyes on. The body was big and brown, but the legs were thin and black, with hairy bristles. Whatever it was began to move in a zigzag pattern, up and down, back and forth, dragging a thread behind it. Although it looked not at all like the little old lady holding her distaff, Ivan was sure it was spinning.

"You're Father Spider!"

"*Tak!*" clicked the creature crossly. "And you are obviously a human thing. Kindly be on your way so I can mend this hole you've made in my web."

"But if it's you," Ivan insisted, "I've come with an invitation."

"I never go out," snapped the spider. "Nor do I let anyone in."

"Please listen, Father Spider," begged Ivan.

The spider, busy tucking and tying his net, paid not the least attention. But Ivan would not give up so easily. He told everything he knew about his village and added a few inventions of his own. The spider yawned. Then Ivan described the mosquitoes, the gnats, the midges, the mites, the flies, and the fleas.

"Such a tempting tale," the spider said. "I seldom accept invitations, for I've my spiderlings to tend to, but you put it so nicely, I cannot refuse."

The spider swung down from his web and began scrambling through the underbrush.

"Wait!" cried Ivan.

"It's rude to be late for supper," called the spider over his shoulder, and was lost to sight.

Ivan feared he was lost too. He did not see one single pebble he had dropped. But, as he searched, he discovered that the thread was still dragging behind Father Spider as he ran. Ivan picked it up and followed, hand over hand, step by step, through the trees, to the road, and all the way back to his village.

Ivan was surprised to find the villagers still in the square. It seemed he'd been gone so long he must have grown at least an inch, but in fact, his whole adventure had taken but one hour and fifty-seven minutes. Everyone was watching this strange thing called a spider. Already it had strung strong lines from the four corners of the square to the well in the middle. By noon, a wonderful web, with one hundred spokes, shimmered in the sunlight. The villagers cheered, and the spider made a small bow.

"I believe it's time to dine," said he.

Ivan, quite hungry after such a walk, went home with the others for a midday meal while Father Spider sat down in the center of his web to await his.

He did not have to wait for long. A gnat, two moths, and a curious cricket brushed against the netting and were held fast.

"You'd scarcely be a mouthful," sniffed the spider, and continued watching and waiting.

Then a huge fly, intent on making off with a mouse, stumbled into the spiderweb.

Tak, tak!" said the spider, pleased. He tiptoed over to the fly.

"Help!" the fly cried.

"How nice of you to join me!" Father Spider carefully wiped his claws.

"Please," begged the fly, struggling against the sticky ropes, "let me loose. I'll give you anything at all."

"You've already given me plenty." The spider patted his stomach.

"But," said the fly, "I've children at home. Dozens and dozens of them."

"So have I," the spider said, remembering all the small spiderlings left behind in the forest.

"And," cried the fly, "left alone, those little fellows will pester the dogs and the cats."

Spider tied a leaf around his waist for a napkin.

"The dogs will growl and the cats will yowl and all the villagers will blame you. They'll chase you away with their sticks."

The spider thought. Perhaps, at this very moment, his spiderlings were misbehaving, too. He sighed. "Very well.

I'll let you go, providing, of course, that you return as soon as your children are cared for."

"Of course! Of course!" cried the fly. "Oh, thank you, Father Spider!"

The spider loosened the knots, and the fly shook its wings and broke free.

"Ho! Ho! Ho!" the fly jeered, hovering high above the web. "Your stupidity is even greater than your appetite! You'll not see me—nor any other—ever again."

And the fly flew off, shrieking, "Stay away from the spider, brothers! He's set a snare to trap you!"

All the mosquitoes and the gnats, the midges and the mites, heard the fly's alarm and hid inside the houses. When the sun went down, the insects came out of their hiding places. In every home they hopped and skittered, fluttered and flitted, nipped and stung. It was worse than before. The menfolk armed themselves with pitchforks and the housewives batted with their brooms. The children pulled the covers over their heads.

"Do something!" shouted the magistrate. None but Father Spider heard him over the buzzing of the bugs.

The spider sat, sad, in his web. He was hungry, for he had long since disposed of the gnat and the two moths. Only the cricket remained. The spider was just about to make a snack of it when a thought struck him with such force that his whole web shook.

"It's possible," said Father Spider, crisscrossing over to the cricket, "to dispatch you in a different fashion!"

The cricket quivered within its bonds.

"You shall go free, friend, and be my messenger."

The cricket chirruped hopefully.

"Play your fiddle and beat the drum," ordered the spider, "and shout the news, 'Spider is dead! Spider is dead! He was called to Kazan and they chopped off his head!'"

"But you aren't dead," objected the cricket.

"No," the spider whispered, "but *you* may be if you don't do as I tell you."

"A bargain!" squeaked the cricket and began hopping around to all the houses and shouting through the shuttered windows, "Spider is dead! Spider is dead!"

Cricket ran up and down the road, playing his fiddle and beating a drum. "He was called to Kazan and they chopped off his head!"

When the other insects heard the cricket's call, they rushed out into the square. The spiderweb was empty.

"We've won! We've won!" sang the fly, and the mosquitoes hummed in chorus, "Father Spider is gone and done!"

The cockroaches waltzed around with the spotted beetles. The mites chased the midges in circles, and the fleas jumped jigs in the square. They all got so giddy that one by one the insects bumped and bumbled into the sticky net. When morning came, every single kind of bug (with the exception of the cricket, who knew better) was hung like a decoration in the spider's web. In the middle sat the spider himself.

"Long live Father Spider!" cried the magistrate and the villagers.

The spider bowed politely once again. But he was much too modest to take all the credit. "It was Ivan who so kindly invited me to dine." The spider smiled as he counted up the company in his web. "Thank you, my friends. No one is more pleased than I with my visit."

Ever after, whatever the weather, the people who live on the steppes have not been so troubled by mosquitoes and gnats or any of their kin. For they make sure to invite Father Spider in to dine. He weaves a web in their rafters and rids them of other, not-so-welcome, guests, while down below, beside the stove, the cricket still fiddles and sings, *"Kazan! Kazan!"*

THE
MAZE

A Pima legend from
Arizona
told by student
Christine Manuel
to Byrd Baylor

In ancient times Se-eh-ha, who is also Elder Brother, needed a safe place to live. He still had a lot of work to do getting the world ready for the Pima and Papago people but he could not do his work because his enemies were always following him.

Even when he went to live in a cave, his enemies followed him. They did not want him to be able to help his people.

Finally he decided to build a home underground in the center of a mountain. At the edge of the mountain anyone could see the opening that led into his house but getting there wasn't as easy as it looked.

Anyone who wanted to find Se-eh-ha had to follow many narrow winding paths that went around and around. His enemies did not know which path to take. If they chose the wrong one they got lost and ran out of air and died down there in the darkness.

While his enemies were searching for him, going around and around in all directions, Se-eh-ha was sitting safely in his cave. The only trouble was that he wanted his friends to be able to come to him without getting lost. He made a map for them and anyone who followed that map could make his way in without getting lost.

Even now the Pima and Papago Indians use that map. The women make a design of it and weave it into baskets so we never forget how to find the right path through life. It can lead you to a safe place.

THE ANT AND THE GRASSHOPPER

a fable by Aesop

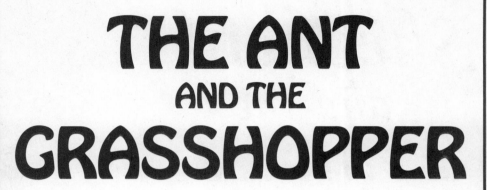

In a field one summer's day a grasshopper was hopping about, chirping and singing to its heart's content. An ant passed by, bearing along with great toil an ear of corn he was taking to the nest.

"Why not come and chat with me," said the grasshopper, "instead of toiling and moiling in that way?"

"I am helping to lay up food for the winter," said the ant, "and recommend you to do the same."

"Why bother about winter?" said the grasshopper. "We have got plenty of food at present." But the ant went on its way and continued its toil. When the winter came the grasshopper had no food, and found itself dying of hunger, while it saw the ants distributing every day corn and grain from the stores they had collected in the summer. Then the grasshopper knew—

It is best to prepare for the days of necessity.

The Shepherd and the Princess

a Puerto Rican folk tale told by Pura Belpré

Once upon a time there reigned a king who was the most obstinate king on earth. His daughter was so beautiful that poets were busy singing her beauty and many a prince and duke had lost his heart to her. But none dared ask her hand in marriage, for they all feared the King greatly.

Then, one day, the King announced that the Princess would marry the one who would bring him three things. First, a glassful of all the waters. Second, a bouquet of all kinds of flowers. Third, a basket of Ay, Ay nuts.

Princes and dukes traveled far and wide to strange lands and soon lost hope of winning the Princess's hand, for nowhere could they find the three things desired by the King.

Now among those who had sung the beauty of the Princess was a shepherd who lived on the hills belonging to the King's land. On many a moonlight night he had stood underneath the Princess's window and sung clear and sweet the simple peasant songs he loved so well. And on many a cool and stormy night the Princess had opened her window and paid the shepherd with one of her lovely smiles.

One day the shepherd heard of the King's announcement and decided to try his luck. He slung his guitar on his back and, with a

merry heart, started on his way. He walked and walked and when
night fell he was in the middle of a forest. Far in the distance he saw
a light. Inside a hut, near a fire, sat a boy watching over a pot and
laughing to himself.

"What are you doing?" asked the shepherd, coming into the
room.

"Oh!" answered the boy. "I am picking up the ones that have
risen and waiting for the ones which are to rise."

The shepherd thought over the boy's answer. Then, he, too, burst
into laughter, for the boy was boiling beans and was taking out the
ones which rose to the top, and waiting for the ones on the bottom
to rise.

"Do you live alone?" asked the shepherd, after watching him for
a while.

"No," answered the boy. "My father and mother are in the fields
gathering yesterday's food."

The shepherd pondered over the strange answer. After a while he
said, "Surely you must be wrong, for you must have eaten yesterday's
food."

The boy looked at him and winked. "My parents are picking the
wool left in the briars as the sheep raced through. Whatever wool
they gather will be sold to pay for the food we ate yesterday. But
who are you," asked the boy, "and what do you do here?"

The shepherd told the boy his story.

"I can help you," said the boy, "if you promise to do as I say."

Following the boy's directions, he soon had the glass of all waters, the bouquet of all flowers, and a basket full of Ay, Ay nuts. With them he arrived at the palace.

When the King heard that the shepherd was in court, he called the Princess, and together they met the shepherd who had been ushered into the courtroom.

"Have you brought the three things?" asked the King.

"Yes, Your Majesty," answered the shepherd, glancing at the Princess shyly.

"Give me the first one," commanded the King.

"Here is a glass of all waters," said the shepherd. "It contains all the waters—waters from the rain, the mountains, the hills, the valleys, the brooks, the springs, and the rivers, for it comes from the sea where all the waters flow."

"Well said," cried the King. "Now give me the second."

The shepherd presented the King a bouquet of all the flowers. "Here, Your Majesty, indeed, is the most beautiful bouquet I could find. It contains flowers of all kinds, put together by the bees in this honeycomb."

"Good, indeed!" merrily shouted the King. "Now for the last one."

"Your Majesty," said the shepherd, "the last thing you will have to pick out yourself. Here in this basket are the Ay, Ay nuts."

The King took the basket and thrust a hand into it to pick out a handful. Something pricked his fingers. "Ay! Ay!" he cried.

"That is correct, Your Majesty," said the shepherd. "For those are the kinds of nuts you told me to bring."

For the boy and the shepherd had placed tiny crabs among the nuts, which now clung to the King's fingers. When the King shook off the last crab, he finally drew out a handful of nuts.

"Ay, Ay nuts, indeed!" he cried.

The Princess roared with laughter. And seeing her so happy, the King took one more look at the shepherd and thought him so clever that right then and there he gave him the Princess's hand in marriage.

It was a fine wedding, I can tell you . . .

Colorin colorado—this story has ended.

THE
RAINHAT

a story retold by Nancy Schimmel

Lillian Oppenheimer tells a version of this story called "The Captain's Hat," from which Nancy Schimmel created "The Rainhat." To fold the hats, Oppenheimer always uses a full sheet of newspaper (approximately 23″ × 30″) folded in half to make a doubled 15″ × 23″ rectangle. Thus, the resulting hats are large enough to put on as you tell the story. And the life jacket at the end is large enough to put on as well!

The folds aren't difficult, but you may wish to practice them once before sharing the story with your class. Give yourself 5–10 minutes to figure out the folds the first time. The trickiest transition is between the pirate hat and the boat (drawing 16). Hold points A and B loosely. As you pull them apart, E moves up and becomes the side of the boat.

It's possible to read the story aloud and do the paper folding as you read, but you may have more fun if you learn the story and tell it in your own words. The sequence of events is logical, and the paper folds follow the sequence of events in the story.

Once there was a little girl who wanted to go outside to play. But her mother wouldn't let her, because it was raining so hard. The little girl didn't want to play inside, because all she had to play with was one piece of paper. So she took the paper and folded it, and folded it, waiting for the rain to stop, but it didn't stop, so she folded the paper some more, and she made herself a rainhat, and put it on, and went outside anyway.

When she got outside, she saw a house burning down, and she wanted to help put out the fire. So she took off her rainhat, and folded it, and folded it, and made herself a firefighter's helmet. Then she went to help put out the fire. She poured on water, and poured on water, until the fire was all out. But the rain kept coming down, and she poured on so much water besides, that there was a flood.

The little girl wanted to go sailing on the flood. But she wouldn't go sailing in a firefighter's hat, so she took it off, and folded it, and made a pirate hat. Then she was all ready to go sailing . . . except . . . she needed a boat. So she took off her pirate hat, and folded it, and folded it, and made a boat. Then she was ready to go sailing. But the flood had covered up lots of things, and the little girl couldn't see them, so she ran right into a car and broke the bow of the boat. She turned the boat around and went right on sailing. Then she ran into a house, and broke the stern off the boat, but she was a brave little girl, and she went on sailing. Then she ran into a library, and broke a hole right in the middle of the boat. Well, with a hole right in the middle of the boat, what happened to the boat? It sank. But the little girl didn't drown, because she was wearing a life jacket.

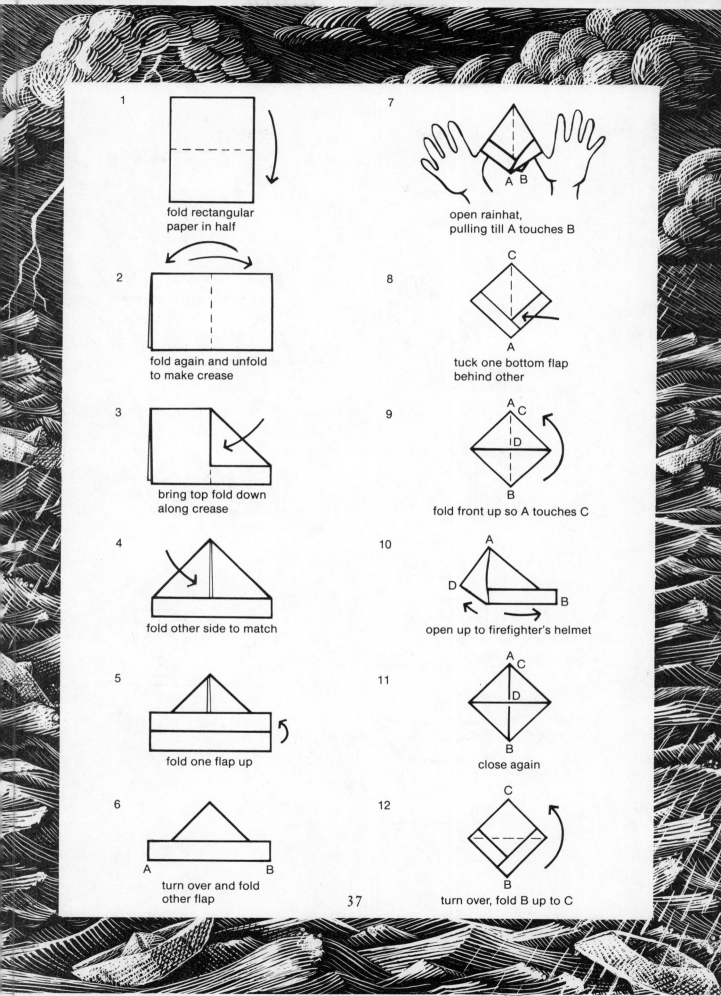

1   fold rectangular
paper in half

2   fold again and unfold
to make crease

3   bring top fold down
along crease

4   fold other side to match

5   fold one flap up

6   turn over and fold
other flap

7   open rainhat,
pulling till A touches B

8   tuck one bottom flap
behind other

9   fold front up so A touches C

10   open up to firefighter's helmet

11   close again

12   turn over, fold B up to C

13

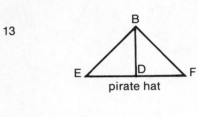

pirate hat

14

open pirate hat,
pull till E touches F

15

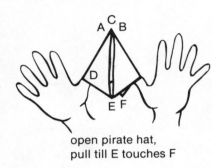

pinch A and B

16

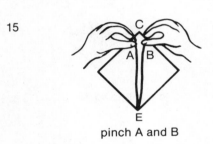

pull A and B out

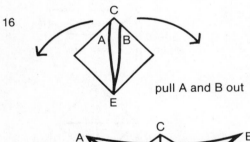

17

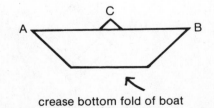

crease bottom fold of boat

18

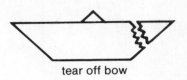

tear off bow

19

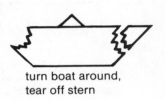

turn boat around,
tear off stern

20

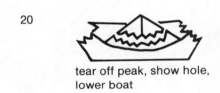

tear off peak, show hole,
lower boat

21

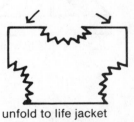

unfold to life jacket
(shoulders still folded),
raise jacket

SOME GREAT BAIT

a tall tale by Joe Hayes

I can't think of a better way to spend a day than sitting on the bank of some favorite fishing hole pulling the fish out of the water. Of course, when I was a boy I didn't get to do that very often, because my mom usually had some work for me to do around the house.

There was one time, though, when she said I could go and fish as long as I wanted. But she told me, "You'd better take along something to eat. You're going to get hungry if you plan on staying all day."

So I went into the kitchen to find something to take along for lunch. I didn't want to bother with making a sandwich—I was looking for something I could grab quick. I searched through the cupboards and found a brand new sack of pretzels. "That'll do," I thought. I grabbed my fishing gear and the sack of pretzels and headed for the pond.

My mom was right. I hadn't been fishing long enough to catch more than two or three fish when I started feeling hungry. So I opened the sack of pretzels and started munching.

Well, of course the pretzels made me thirsty and I began to wish I'd brought along something to drink. But I hadn't, so the only thing to do was to drink a little water from the pond. It was good clear spring water, so I knew it wouldn't do me any harm. Then, as I stooped over to get a sip from the pond, a

question popped into my mind. I thought, "I wonder if fish like pretzels?"

I snapped a little piece off a pretzel and flipped it into the pond. *Blip!* A fish came up and swallowed the piece of pretzel. "That's great!" I said to myself. "They love pretzels!"

I tore open the pretzel sack and ground them up in my hands. Then I threw handful after handful of pretzel crumbs into the pond. The fish just made the water boil as they went after the pretzels, and naturally the pretzels made the fish thirsty too. So they drank water from the pond, just like I did.

They ate pretzels and drank water, ate more pretzels and drank more water, and the pond was getting lower and lower all the time. I just sat back and watched with a big grin on my face. And it may be hard for you to believe, but the fish kept going until they drank up every drop of water in the pond. I just walked around and picked fish up off the bottom of the dry hole where the pond had once been.

So you can talk to me about your favorite fishing bait—worms or eggs or corn or whatever—but as far as I'm concerned, it's hard to find a better bait than pretzels. Unless maybe it's raisins.

You see, on another very similar occasion all I could find to make a quick lunch was a sack of raisins. I knew my mom would like the idea of my taking raisins along to eat because she always told me raisins were good for me. "They put iron in your blood," she'd say.

Once again I thought I'd see if fish had any taste for my food. I tossed a raisin into the pond. Sure enough—they liked raisins even better than pretzels.

All the while they were eating my raisins I was thinking, "Won't your mommas be proud of you for getting all that iron in your blood?" And then I got an idea. I reached into my back pocket and pulled out a magnet. I held it under the water, and the next thing I knew there was a fish stuck to it.

Yeah! Those fish had so much iron in their blood from eating my raisins I spent the rest of the afternoon pulling them out of the pond with a magnet! That was a little more interesting than just picking fish up from the dry ground, so I guess raisins are a little better bait than pretzels.

40

THE TAILOR

a European folk tale retold by Doug Lipman

Long ago, there was a poor, clever tailor.

One day, he managed to buy a fine piece of cloth for himself.

So he measured, he figured, he cut, and he sewed.

When he was done, he had made himself a splendid coat. He loved the coat so much that he wore it every day, no matter the weather, no matter where he went. He wore it and wore it until it was worn out.

Well, it was almost worn out. He looked closely at the coat. There were a few pieces left of that splendid coat that were not worn out.

So he measured, he figured, he cut, and he sewed.

When he was done, he had made himself a splendid vest.

He loved the vest so much that he wore it every day, no matter the weather, no matter where he went. He wore it and wore it until it was worn out.

Well, it was almost worn out. He looked closely at the vest. There were a few pieces left of that splendid vest that were not worn out.

So he measured, he figured, he cut, and he sewed.

When he was done, he had made himself a splendid, cloth-covered button. He loved the button so much that he wore it every day, no matter the weather, no matter where he went. He wore it and wore it until it was worn out.

Yes! It was completely worn out!

He looked closely. There were no pieces left of that splendid button—not a single thread!

What could he do?

He was a very clever tailor. So he made the button into . . . a story. It was a splendid story. He told it every day.

And the story never, ever wore out.

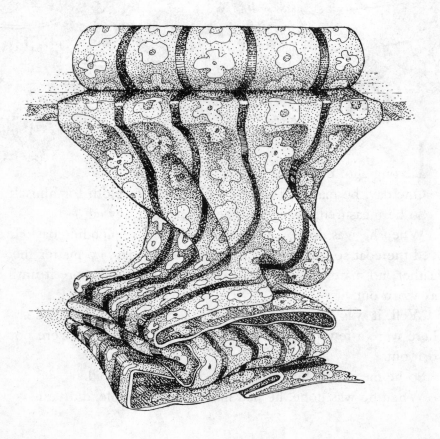

THE **WALRUS** AND THE **CARPENTER**

a poem by Lewis Carroll

The sun was shining on the sea,
　　Shining with all his might:
He did his very best to make
　　The billows smooth and bright—
And this was odd, because it was
　　The middle of the night.

The moon was shining sulkily,
　　Because she thought the sun
Had got no business to be there
　　After the day was done—
"It's very rude of him," she said,
　　"To come and spoil the fun!"

The sea was wet as wet could be,
　　The sands were dry as dry.
You could not see a cloud, because
　　No cloud was in the sky:
No birds were flying overhead—
　　There were no birds to fly.

The Walrus and the Carpenter
　　Were walking close at hand:
They wept like anything to see
　　Such quantities of sand:
"If this were only cleared away,"
　　They said, "it *would* be grand!"

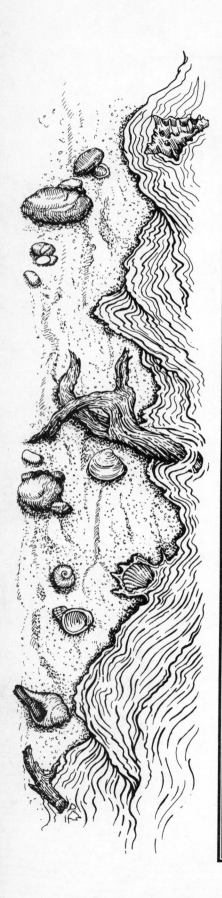

"If seven maids with seven mops
    Swept it for half a year,
Do you suppose," the Walrus said,
    "That they could get it clear?"
"I doubt it," said the Carpenter,
    And shed a bitter tear.

"O Oysters, come and walk with us!"
    The Walrus did beseech.
"A pleasant walk, a pleasant talk,
    Along the briny beach:
We cannot do with more than four,
    To give a hand to each."

The eldest Oyster looked at him,
    But never a word he said:
The eldest Oyster winked his eye,
    And shook his heavy head—
Meaning to say he did not choose
    To leave the oyster-bed.

But four young Oysters hurried up,
    All eager for the treat:
Their coats were brushed, their faces washed,
    Their shoes were clean and neat—
And this was odd, because, you know,
    They hadn't any feet.

Four other oysters followed them,
    And yet another four;
And thick and fast they came at last,
    And more, and more, and more—
All hopping through the frothy waves,
    And scrambling to the shore.

The Walrus and the Carpenter
    Walked a mile or so,
And then they rested on a rock
    Conveniently low:
And all the little Oysters stood
    And waited in a row.

"The time has come," the Walrus said,
    "To talk of many things:
Of shoes—and ships—and sealing-wax—
    Of cabbages—and kings—
And why the sea is boiling hot—
    And whether pigs have wings."

"But wait a bit," the Oysters cried,
    "Before we have our chat;
For some of us are out of breath,
    And all of us are fat!"
"No hurry!" said the Carpenter.
    They thanked him much for that.

"A loaf of bread," the Walrus said,
    "Is what we chiefly need:
Pepper and vinegar besides
    Are very good indeed—
Now, if you're ready, Oysters dear,
    We can begin to feed."

"But not on us!" the Oysters cried,
    Turning a little blue.
"After such kindness, that would be
    A dismal thing to do!"
"The night is fine," the Walrus said.
    "Do you admire the view?

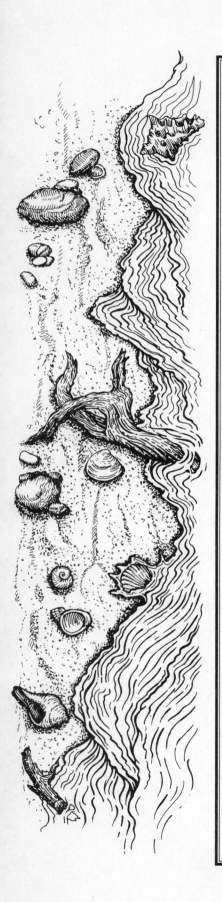

"It was so kind of you to come!
    And you are very nice!"
The Carpenter said nothing but
    "Cut us another slice.
I wish you were not quite so deaf—
    I've had to ask you twice!"

"It seems a shame," the Walrus said,
    "To play them such a trick.
After we've brought them out so far,
    And made them trot so quick!"
The Carpenter said nothing but
    "The butter's spread too thick!"

"I weep for you," the Walrus said:
    "I deeply sympathize."
With sobs and tears he sorted out
    Those of the largest size,
Holding his pocket-handkerchief
    Before his streaming eyes.

"O Oysters," said the Carpenter,
    "You've had a pleasant run!
Shall we be trotting home again?"
    But answer came there none—
And this was scarcely odd, because
    They'd eaten every one.

WHY THE BABY SAYS, "GOO-GOO"

*a Penobscot tale from the Northeastern United States
retold by Floating Eaglefeather*

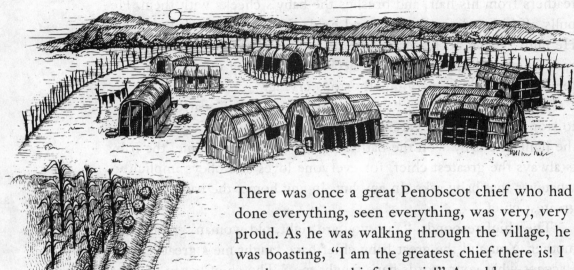

There was once a great Penobscot chief who had done everything, seen everything, was very, very proud. As he was walking through the village, he was boasting, "I am the greatest chief there is! I am the greatest chief there is!" An old woman came up to the chief and said, "No, you're not. I know a chief who is greater than you."

The great chief reeled back and said, "What! Who is this great chief?! There is no chief greater than I am!"

The old woman said, "Um, well, if you come to my house tomorrow at noon, I will introduce you to this great chief."

The chief said, "Very well, old woman, grandmother, I will be there tomorrow at noon and we will see who is the greater chief."

The chief went home and slept very soundly, in order to gain strength and beauty during the night. In the morning, he did his work around the house, put on his finest clothing, his eagle and hawk feathers, medicine bundles, necklaces, and beads. When he was finished, he knew that, if it was to be a fight of strength, he would win, and, if it was to be a fight of beauty, he would win. He went to the old woman's home and called, "Old woman, grandmother, I am here, it is noon."

"Come in, come in."

The great chief walks in, sees the old woman, sitting against the wall, and sees a baby crawling around on the floor. "Where is the great chieftain of whom you spoke, has he or she not arrived yet?"

The old woman motions to the baby and says, "Oh, this is the great chief."

The chief yells angrily, "What do you mean, are you trying to play a trick on me, this is just a baby!"

The baby, frightened by the sudden, loud, angry voice, begins to cry. The chief is flustered by the crying, pulls his eagle and hawk feathers from his hair, and brushes the baby's cheeks with them. He pulls off his medicine bundles and holds them under the baby's nose. He pulls off the necklaces and beads and jingles them in the baby's ears. The baby, listening to the necklaces, smelling the bundles, and feeling the feathers, very quietly stops crying.

The old woman says, "You see, even you, 'the Great Chief,' had to stop talking to take care of the needs of the baby. The baby won the fight, the baby won the battle. In any hut, in any home, the baby is always the greatest chief, for everyone loves and obeys implicitly whatever that baby asks. In any hut, in any home, the baby is the greatest chief."

The chief responds, "Yes, you are right, old woman, grandmother. You and the great baby chief have taught me a great lesson. I accept what your words have taught me." The chief began to put the necklaces and bundles around his neck, the eagle and hawk feathers back into his hair, and was just turning to leave. At this moment, the baby said, "Goo-goo!" This was the baby's victory cry, and ever since then, babies all over the world say, "Goo-goo." Thanks to this story, we know what that means. The baby is saying, "I am the world's greatest chief—Goo-Goo!"

CHARLOTTE'S WEB

an excerpt from the book by E. B. White

Chapter I
BEFORE BREAKFAST

"Where's Papa going with that ax?" said Fern to her mother as they were setting the table for breakfast.

"Out to the hoghouse," replied Mrs. Arable. "Some pigs were born last night."

"I don't see why he needs an ax," continued Fern, who was only eight.

"Well," said her mother, "one of the pigs is a runt. It's very small and weak, and it will never amount to anything. So your father has decided to do away with it."

"Do *away* with it?" shrieked Fern. "You mean *kill* it? Just because it's smaller than the others?"

Mrs. Arable put a pitcher of cream on the table. "Don't yell, Fern!" she said. "Your father is right. The pig would probably die anyway."

Fern pushed a chair out of the way and ran outdoors. The grass was wet and the earth smelled of springtime. Fern's sneakers were sopping by the time she caught up with her father.

"Please don't kill it!" she sobbed. "It's unfair."

Mr. Arable stopped walking.

"Fern," he said gently, "you will have to learn to control yourself."

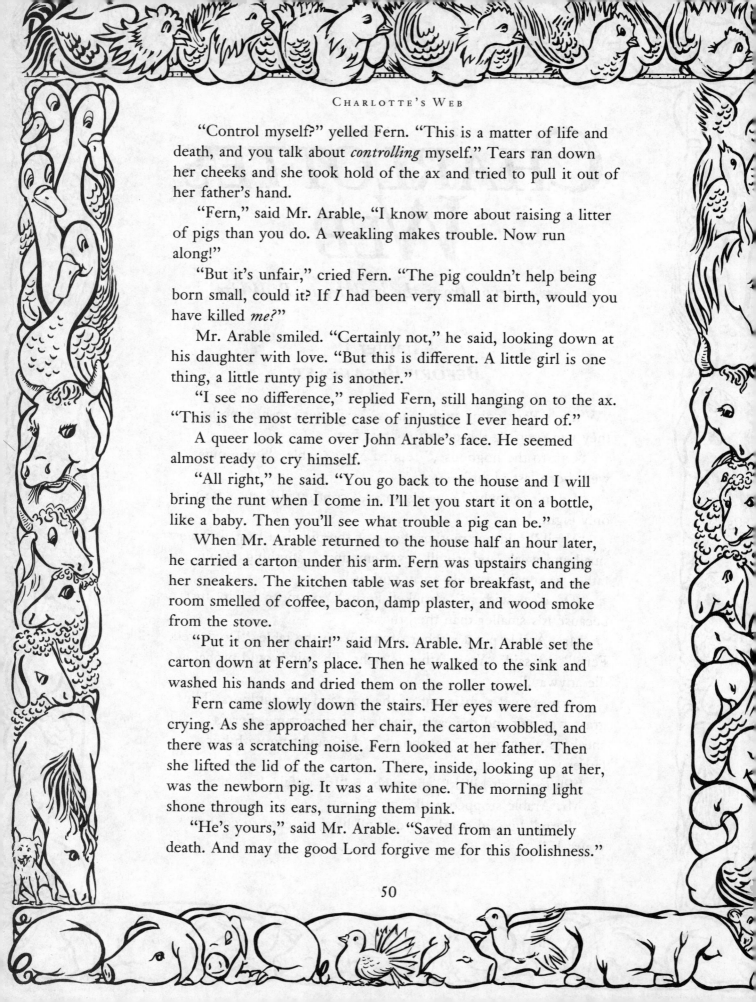

"Control myself?" yelled Fern. "This is a matter of life and death, and you talk about *controlling* myself." Tears ran down her cheeks and she took hold of the ax and tried to pull it out of her father's hand.

"Fern," said Mr. Arable, "I know more about raising a litter of pigs than you do. A weakling makes trouble. Now run along!"

"But it's unfair," cried Fern. "The pig couldn't help being born small, could it? If *I* had been very small at birth, would you have killed *me?*"

Mr. Arable smiled. "Certainly not," he said, looking down at his daughter with love. "But this is different. A little girl is one thing, a little runty pig is another."

"I see no difference," replied Fern, still hanging on to the ax. "This is the most terrible case of injustice I ever heard of."

A queer look came over John Arable's face. He seemed almost ready to cry himself.

"All right," he said. "You go back to the house and I will bring the runt when I come in. I'll let you start it on a bottle, like a baby. Then you'll see what trouble a pig can be."

When Mr. Arable returned to the house half an hour later, he carried a carton under his arm. Fern was upstairs changing her sneakers. The kitchen table was set for breakfast, and the room smelled of coffee, bacon, damp plaster, and wood smoke from the stove.

"Put it on her chair!" said Mrs. Arable. Mr. Arable set the carton down at Fern's place. Then he walked to the sink and washed his hands and dried them on the roller towel.

Fern came slowly down the stairs. Her eyes were red from crying. As she approached her chair, the carton wobbled, and there was a scratching noise. Fern looked at her father. Then she lifted the lid of the carton. There, inside, looking up at her, was the newborn pig. It was a white one. The morning light shone through its ears, turning them pink.

"He's yours," said Mr. Arable. "Saved from an untimely death. And may the good Lord forgive me for this foolishness."

Fern couldn't take her eyes off the tiny pig. "Oh," she whispered. "Oh, *look* at him! He's absolutely perfect."

She closed the carton carefully. First she kissed her father, then she kissed her mother. Then she opened the lid again, lifted the pig out, and held it against her cheek. At this moment her brother Avery came into the room. Avery was ten. He was heavily armed—an air rifle in one hand, a wooden dagger in the other.

"What's that?" he demanded. "What's Fern got?"

"She's got a guest for breakfast," said Mrs. Arable. "Wash your hands and face, Avery!"

"Let's see it!" said Avery, setting his gun down. "You call that miserable thing a pig? That's a *fine* specimen of a pig—it's no bigger than a white rat."

"Wash up and eat your breakfast, Avery!" said his mother. "The school bus will be along in half an hour."

"Can I have a pig, too, Pop?" asked Avery.

"No, I only distribute pigs to early risers," said Mr. Arable. "Fern was up at daylight, trying to rid the world of injustice. As a result, she now has a pig. A small one, to be sure, but nevertheless a pig. It just shows what can happen if a person gets out of bed promptly. Let's eat!"

But Fern couldn't eat until her pig had had a drink of milk. Mrs. Arable found a baby's nursing bottle and a rubber nipple. She poured warm milk into the bottle, fitted the nipple over the top, and handed it to Fern. "Give him his breakfast!" she said.

A minute later, Fern was seated on the floor in the corner of the kitchen with her infant between her knees, teaching it to suck from the bottle. The pig, although tiny, had a good appetite and caught on quickly.

The school bus honked from the road.

"Run!" commanded Mrs. Arable, taking the pig from Fern and slipping a doughnut into her hand. Avery grabbed his gun and another doughnut.

The children ran out to the road and climbed into the bus. Fern took no notice of the others in the bus. She just sat and stared out of the window, thinking what a blissful world it was and how lucky she was to have entire charge of a pig. By the time the bus reached school, Fern had named her pet, selecting the most beautiful name she could think of.

"Its name is Wilbur," she whispered to herself.

She was still thinking about the pig when the teacher said: "Fern, what is the capital of Pennsylvania?"

"Wilbur," replied Fern, dreamily. The pupils giggled. Fern blushed.

Chapter II
WILBUR

Fern loved Wilbur more than anything. She loved to stroke him, to feed him, to put him to bed. Every morning, as soon as she got up, she warmed his milk, tied his bib on, and held the bottle for him. Every afternoon, when the school bus stopped in front of her house, she jumped out and ran to the kitchen to fix another bottle for him. She fed him again at suppertime, and again just before going to bed. Mrs. Arable gave him a feeding around noontime each day, when Fern was away in school. Wilbur loved his milk, and he was never happier than when Fern was warming up a bottle for him. He would stand and gaze up at her with adoring eyes.

For the first few days of his life, Wilbur was allowed to live in a box near the stove in the kitchen. Then, when Mrs. Arable complained, he was moved to a bigger box in the woodshed. At two weeks of age, he was moved outdoors. It was apple-blossom time, and the days were getting warmer. Mr. Arable fixed a small yard specially for Wilbur under an apple tree, and gave him a large wooden box full of straw, with a doorway cut in it so he could walk in and out as he pleased.

"Won't he be cold at night?" asked Fern.

"No," said her father. "You watch and see what he does."

Carrying a bottle of milk, Fern sat down under the apple tree inside the yard. Wilbur ran to her and she held the bottle for him while he sucked. When he had finished the last drop, he grunted and walked sleepily into the box. Fern peered through the door. Wilbur was poking the straw with his snout. In a short time he had dug a tunnel in the straw. He crawled into the tunnel and disappeared from sight, completely covered with straw. Fern was enchanted. It relieved her mind to know that her baby would sleep covered up, and would stay warm.

Every morning after breakfast, Wilbur walked out to the road with Fern and waited with her till the bus came. She would wave good-bye to him, and he would stand and watch the bus until it vanished around a turn. While Fern was in school, Wilbur was shut up inside his yard. But as soon as she got home in the afternoon, she would take him out and he would follow her around the place. If she went into the house, Wilbur went, too. If she went upstairs, Wilbur would wait at the bottom step until she came down again. If she took her doll for a walk in the doll carriage, Wilbur followed along. Sometimes, on these journeys, Wilbur would get tired, and Fern would pick him up and put him in the carriage alongside the doll. He liked this. And if he was *very* tired, he would close his eyes and go to sleep under the doll's blanket. He looked cute when his eyes were closed, because his lashes were so long. The doll would close her eyes, too, and Fern would wheel the carriage very slowly and smoothly so as not to wake her infants.

One warm afternoon, Fern and Avery put on bathing suits and went down to the brook for a swim. Wilbur tagged along at Fern's heels. When she waded into the brook, Wilbur waded in with her. He found the water quite cold—too cold for his liking. So while the children swam and played and splashed water at each other, Wilbur amused himself in the mud along the edge of the brook, where it was warm and moist and delightfully sticky and oozy.

Every day was a happy day, and every night was peaceful.

Wilbur was what farmers call a spring pig, which simply means that he was born in springtime. When he was five weeks old, Mr. Arable said he was now big enough to sell, and would have to be sold. Fern broke down and wept. But her father was firm about it. Wilbur's appetite had increased; he was beginning to eat scraps of food in addition to milk. Mr. Arable was not willing to provide for him any longer. He had already sold Wilbur's ten brothers and sisters.

"He's got to go, Fern," he said. "You have had your fun raising a baby pig, but Wilbur is not a baby any longer and he has got to be sold."

"Call up the Zuckermans," suggested Mrs. Arable to Fern. "Your Uncle Homer sometimes raises a pig. And if Wilbur goes there to live, you can walk down the road and visit him as often as you like."

"How much money should I ask for him?" Fern wanted to know.

"Well," said her father, "he's a runt. Tell your Uncle Homer you've got a pig you'll sell for six dollars, and see what he says."

It was soon arranged. Fern phoned and got her Aunt Edith, and her Aunt Edith hollered for Uncle Homer, and Uncle Homer came in from the barn and talked to Fern. When he heard that the price was only six dollars, he said he would buy the pig. Next day Wilbur was taken from his home under the apple tree and went to live in a manure pile in the cellar of the Zuckerman's barn.

Chapter III
ESCAPE

The barn was very large. It was very old. It smelled of hay and it smelled of manure. It smelled of the perspiration of tired horses and the wonderful sweet breath of patient cows. It often had a sort of peaceful smell—as though nothing bad could happen ever again in the world. It smelled of grain and of harness dressing and of axle grease and of rubber boots and of new rope. And whenever the cat was given a fish-head to eat, the barn would smell of fish. But mostly it smelled of hay, for there was always hay in the great loft up overhead. And there was always hay being pitched down to the cows and the horses and the sheep.

The barn was pleasantly warm in winter when the animals spent most of their time indoors, and it was pleasantly cool in summer when the big doors stood wide open to the breeze. The barn had stalls on the main floor for the work horses, tie-ups on the main floor for the cows, a sheepfold down below for the sheep, a pigpen down below for Wilbur, and it was full of all sorts of things that you find in barns: ladders, grindstones, pitch forks, monkey wrenches, scythes, lawn mowers, snow shovels, ax handles, milk pails, water buckets, empty grain sacks, and rusty rat traps. It was the kind of barn that swallows like to build their nests in. It was the kind of barn that children like to play in. And the whole thing was owned by Fern's uncle, Mr. Homer L. Zuckerman.

Wilbur's new home was in the lower part of the barn, directly underneath the cows. Mr. Zuckerman knew that a manure pile is a good place to keep a young pig. Pigs need warmth, and it was warm and comfortable down there in the barn cellar on the south side.

Fern came almost every day to visit him. She found an old milking stool that had been discarded, and she placed the stool in the sheepfold next to Wilbur's pen. Here she sat quietly during the long afternoons, thinking and listening and watching Wilbur. The sheep soon got to know her and trust her. So did the geese, who lived with the sheep. All the animals trusted her, she was so quiet and friendly. Mr. Zuckerman did not allow her to take Wilbur out, and he did not allow her to get into the pigpen. But he told Fern that she could sit on the stool and watch Wilbur as long as she wanted to. It made her happy just to be near the pig, and it made Wilbur happy to know that she was sitting there, right outside his pen. But he never had any fun—no walks, no rides, no swims.

One afternoon in June, when Wilbur was almost two months old, he wandered out into his small yard outside the barn. Fern had not arrived for her usual visit. Wilbur stood in the sun feeling lonely and bored.

"There's never anything to do around here," he thought. He walked slowly to his food trough and sniffed to see if anything had been overlooked at lunch. He found a small strip of potato skin and ate it. His back itched, so he leaned against the fence and rubbed against the boards. When he tired of this, he walked indoors, climbed to the top of the manure pile, and sat down. He didn't feel like going to sleep, he didn't feel like digging, he was tired of standing still, tired of lying down. "I'm less than two months old and I'm tired of living," he said. He walked out to the yard again.

"When I'm out here," he said, "there's no place to go but in. When I'm indoors, there's no place to go but out in the yard."

"That's where you're wrong, my friend, my friend," said a voice.

Wilbur looked through the fence and saw the goose standing there.

"You don't have to stay in that dirty-little dirty-little dirty-little yard," said the goose, who talked rather fast. "One of the boards is loose. Push on it, push-push-push on it, and come on out!"

"What?" said Wilbur. "Say it slower!"

"At-at-at, at the risk of repeating myself," said the goose, "I suggest that you come on out. It's wonderful out here."

"Did you say a board was loose?"

"That I did, that I did," said the goose.

Wilbur walked up to the fence and saw that the goose was right—one board was loose. He put his head down, shut his eyes, and pushed. The board gave way. In a minute he had squeezed through the fence and was standing in the long grass outside his yard. The goose chuckled.

"How does it feel to be free?" she asked.

"I like it," said Wilbur. "That is, I *guess* I like it." Actually, Wilbur felt queer to be outside his fence, with nothing between him and the big world.

"Where do you think I'd better go?"

"Anywhere you like, anywhere you like," said the goose. "Go down through the orchard, root up the sod! Go down through the garden, dig up the radishes! Root up everything! Eat grass! Look for corn! Look for oats! Run all over! Skip and dance, jump and prance! Go down through the orchard and stroll in the woods! The world is a wonderful place when you're young."

"I can see that," replied Wilbur. He gave a jump in the air, twirled, ran a few steps, stopped, looked all around, sniffed the smells of afternoon, and then set off walking down through the orchard. Pausing in the shade of an apple tree, he put his strong snout into the ground and began pushing, digging, and rooting. He felt very happy. He had plowed up quite a piece of ground before anyone noticed him. Mrs. Zuckerman was the first to see him. She saw him from the kitchen window, and she immediately shouted for the men.

"Ho-*mer*!" she cried. "Pig's out! Homer! Lurvy! Pig's out! Homer! Lurvy! Pig's out. He's down there under that apple tree."

"Now the trouble starts," thought Wilbur. "Now I'll catch it."

The goose heard the racket and she, too, started hollering. "Run-run-run downhill, make for the woods, the woods!" she shouted to Wilbur. "They'll never-never-never catch you in the woods."

The cocker spaniel heard the commotion and he ran out from the barn to join the chase. Mr. Zuckerman heard, and he came out of the machine shed where he was mending a tool. Lurvy, the hired man, heard the noise and came up from the asparagus patch where he was pulling weeds. Everybody walked toward Wilbur and Wilbur didn't know what to do. The woods seemed a long way off, and anyway, he had never been down there in the woods and wasn't sure he would like it.

"Get around behind him, Lurvy," said Mr. Zuckerman, "and drive him toward the barn! And take it easy—don't rush him! I'll go and get a bucket of slops."

The news of Wilbur's escape spread rapidly among the animals on the place. Whenever any creature broke loose on Zuckerman's farm, the event was of great interest to the others. The goose shouted to the nearest cow that Wilbur was free, and soon all the cows knew. Then one of the cows told one of the sheep, and soon all the sheep knew. The lambs learned about it from their mothers. The horses, in their stalls in the barn, pricked up their ears when they heard the goose hollering; and soon the horses had caught on to what was happening. "Wilbur's out," they said. Every animal stirred and lifted its head and became excited to know that one of his friends had got free and was no longer penned up or tied fast.

Wilbur didn't know what to do or which way to run. It seemed as though everybody was after him. "If this is what it's like to be free," he thought, "I believe I'd rather be penned up in my own yard."

The cocker spaniel was sneaking up on him from one side, Lurvy the hired man was sneaking up on him from the other side. Mrs. Zuckerman stood ready to head him off if he started for the garden, and now Mr. Zuckerman was coming down toward him carrying a pail. "This is really awful," thought Wilbur. "Why doesn't Fern come?" He began to cry.

The goose took command and began to give orders.

"Don't just stand there, Wilbur! Dodge about, dodge about!" cried the goose. "Skip around, run toward me, slip in and out, in and out, in and out! Make for the woods! Twist and turn!"

The cocker spaniel sprang for Wilbur's hind leg. Wilbur jumped and ran. Lurvy reached out and grabbed. Mrs. Zuckerman screamed at Lurvy. The goose cheered for Wilbur. Wilbur dodged between Lurvy's legs. Lurvy missed Wilbur and grabbed the spaniel instead. "Nicely done, nicely done!" cried the goose. "Try it again, try it again!"

"Run downhill!" suggested the cows.

"Run toward me!" yelled the gander.

"Run uphill!" cried the sheep.

"Turn and twist!" honked the goose.

"Jump and dance!" said the rooster.

"Look out for Lurvy!" called the cows.

"Look out for Zuckerman!" yelled the gander.

"Watch out for the dog!" cried the sheep.

"Listen to me, listen to me!" screamed the goose.

Poor Wilbur was dazed and frightened by this hullabaloo. He didn't like being the center of all this fuss. He tried to follow the instructions his friends were giving him, but he couldn't run downhill and uphill at the same time, and he couldn't turn and twist when he was jumping and dancing, and he was crying so hard he could barely see anything that was happening. After all, Wilbur was a very young pig—not much more than a baby, really. He wished Fern were there to take him in her arms and comfort him. When he looked up and saw Mr. Zuckerman standing quite close to him, holding a pail of warm slops, he felt relieved. He lifted his nose and sniffed. The smell was delicious—warm milk, potato skins, wheat middlings, Kellogg's Corn Flakes, and a popover left from the Zuckermans' breakfast.

"Come, pig!" said Mr. Zuckerman, tapping the pail. "Come, pig!"

Wilbur took a step toward the pail.

"No-no-no!" said the goose. "It's the old pail trick, Wilbur. Don't fall for it, don't fall for it! He's trying to lure you back into captivity-ivity. He's appealing to your stomach."

Wilbur didn't care. The food smelled appetizing. He took another step toward the pail.

"Pig, pig!" said Mr. Zuckerman in a kind voice, and began walking slowly toward the barnyard, looking all about him innocently, as if he didn't know that a little white pig was following along behind him.

"You'll be sorry-sorry-sorry," called the goose.

Wilbur didn't care. He kept walking toward the pail of slops.

"You'll miss your freedom," honked the goose. "An hour of freedom is worth a barrel of slops."

Wilbur didn't care.

When Mr. Zuckerman reached the pigpen, he climbed over the fence and poured the slops into the trough. Then he pulled the loose board away from the fence, so that there was a wide hole for Wilbur to walk through.

"Reconsider, reconsider!" cried the goose.

Wilbur paid no attention. He stepped through the fence into his yard. He walked to the trough and took a long drink of slops, sucking in the milk hungrily and chewing the popover. It was good to be home again.

While Wilbur ate, Lurvy fetched a hammer and some 8-penny nails and nailed the board in place. Then he and Mr. Zuckerman leaned lazily on the fence and Mr. Zuckerman scratched Wilbur's back with a stick.

"He's quite a pig," said Lurvy.

"Yes, he'll make a good pig," said Mr. Zuckerman.

Wilbur heard the words of praise. He felt the warm milk inside his stomach. He felt the pleasant rubbing of the stick along his itchy back. He felt peaceful and happy and sleepy. This had been a tiring afternoon. It was still only about four o'clock but Wilbur was ready for bed.

"I'm really too young to go out into the woods alone," he thought as he lay down.

STRAWBERRIES

*a Cherokee legend from the Southern United States
retold by Gayle Ross*

Long ago, in the very first days of the world, there lived the first man and the first woman. They lived together as husband and wife, and they loved one another dearly.

But one day, they quarreled. Although neither later could remember what the quarrel was about, the pain grew stronger with every word that was spoken, until finally, in anger and in grief, the woman left their home and began walking away—to the east, toward the rising sun.

The man sat alone in his house. But as time went by, he grew lonelier and lonelier. The anger left him and all that remained was a terrible grief and despair, and he began to cry.

A spirit heard the man crying and took pity on him. The spirit said, "Man, why do you cry?"

The man said, "My wife has left me."

The spirit said, "Why did your woman leave?"

The man just hung his head and said nothing.

The spirit asked, "You quarreled with her?"

And the man nodded.

"Would you quarrel with her again?" asked the spirit.

The man said, "No." He wanted only to live with his wife as they had lived before—in peace, in happiness, and in love.

"I have seen your woman," the spirit said. "She is walking to the east toward the rising sun."

The man followed his wife, but he could not overtake her. Everyone knows an angry woman walks fast.

Finally, the spirit said, "I'll go ahead and see if I can make her slow her steps." So the spirit found the woman walking, her footsteps fast and angry and her gaze fixed straight ahead. There was pain in her heart.

The spirit saw some huckleberry bushes growing along the trail, so with a wave of his hand, he made the bushes burst into bloom and ripen into fruit. But the woman's gaze remained fixed. She looked neither to the right nor the left, and she didn't see the berries. Her footsteps didn't slow.

Again, the spirit waved his hand, and one by one, *all* of the berries growing along the trail burst into bloom and ripened into fruit. But still, the woman's gaze remained fixed. She saw nothing but her anger and pain, and her footsteps didn't slow.

And again, the spirit waved his hand, and, one by one, the trees of the forest—the peach, the pear, the apple, the wild cherry—burst into bloom and ripened into fruit. But still, the woman's eyes remained fixed, and even still, she saw nothing but her anger and pain. And her footsteps didn't slow.

Then finally, the spirit thought, "I will create an entirely new fruit—one that grows very, very close to the ground so the woman must forget her anger and bend her head for a moment." So the spirit waved his hand, and a thick green carpet began to grow along the trail. Then the carpet became starred with tiny white flowers, and each flower gradually ripened into a berry that was the color and shape of the human heart.

As the woman walked, she crushed the tiny berries, and the delicious aroma came up through her nose. She stopped and looked down, and she saw the berries. She picked one and ate it, and she discovered its taste was as sweet as love itself. So she began walking slowly, picking berries as she went, and as she leaned down to pick a berry, she saw her husband coming behind her.

The anger had gone from her heart, and all that remained was the love she had always known. So she stopped for him, and together, they picked and ate the berries. Finally, they returned to their home where they lived out their days in peace, happiness, and love.

And that's how the world's very first strawberries brought peace between men and women in the world, and why to this day they are called the berries of love.

UDALA TREE

*an Ibo folk tale from West Africa
retold by Margaret Read MacDonald*

There was an orphan boy
who had no mother or father of his own.
He lived with his stepmother
and two stepbrothers.

Now whenever there was food to be had
the stepmother and the stepbrothers ate the good food
and gave the orphan boy only the scraps.

Whenever there was *work* to be done
the stepmother and the stepbrothers
    would do only the lightest work
and give all the hardest work to the Boy.

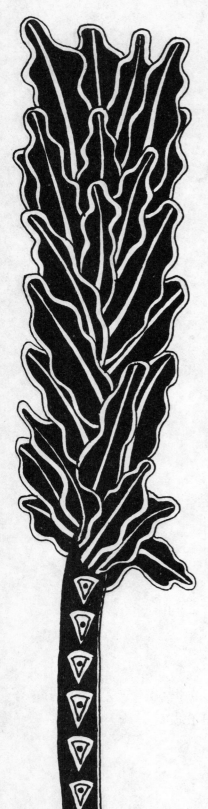

Every day he had to sweep the compound,
hoe the garden,
and bring water from the river.

One day when the Boy was sweeping the compound
he found the seed of an Udala tree
lodged in a crack in the ground.

The Boy owned *nothing* of his own.
He thought I will *keep* this shiny Udala seed.
It will be something that *belongs to me.*

That night when the Boy slept
he put the Udala seed under his pillow.
And while he slept he had a *dream.*

The Boy dreamed that an Udala tree
grew from the tiny seed under his pillow
and spread its branches over his head.

The next morning
the Boy took the Udala seed to the garden.
He made a tiny hole and planted the seed.
He covered it over. . . .
He brought water from the stream and watered it.

Then the Boy sat down
and he began to chant.

"Udala GROW!
NDA!
Udala GROW!
NDA!
Grow for motherless child!
NDA!
Grow for fatherless child!
NDA!

64

The Earth is a place of call.
NDA!
Man stops here and goes on."

And as the Boy chanted
a tiny shoot began to grow from the Udala seed.

The Boy chanted louder.

"Udala GROW!
NDA!
Udala GROW!
NDA!
Grow for motherless child!
NDA!
Grow for fatherless child!
NDA!
The Earth is a place of call.
NDA!
Man stops here and goes on.
NDA!"

And as the Boy chanted
the *Udala* tree began to grow . . .
it grew taller than the Boy's head.

The Boy became EXCITED!

"Udala GROW!
NDA!
Udala GROW!
NDA!
Grow for motherless child!
NDA!
Grow for fatherless child!
NDA!

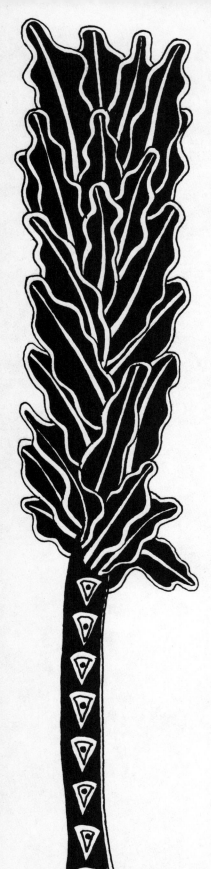

The Earth is a place of call.
NDA!
Man stops here and goes on.
NDA!"

Before his very eyes
that seed grew until it became a great Udala tree.
And spread its branches over his head.

The Boy sat in the shade of his *very own* Udala tree.
And he was *happy*.

Then the Boy thought
"What if the tree should bear *fruit?*"

So the Boy chanted:

"Udala FRUIT!
NDA!
Udala FRUIT!
NDA!
Fruit for motherless child!
NDA!
Fruit for fatherless child!
NDA!
The Earth is a place of call.
NDA!
Man stops here and goes on.
NDA!"

Then over his head
Udala fruit grew on the branches.
Tiny green Udala fruit covered the tree.

The Boy chanted for the fruit to *ripen*.

"Udala RIPEN!
NDA!
Udala RIPEN!
NDA!
Ripen for motherless child!
NDA!
Ripen for fatherless child!
NDA!
The Earth is a place of call.
NDA!
Man stops here and goes on.
NDA!"

All through the Udala tree
the fruit turned a ripe yellowish brown.

But the Boy could not reach the fruit.
He called for the fruit to . . . *drop*.

"Udala DROP!
NDA!
Udala DROP!
NDA!
Drop for motherless child!
NDA!
Drop for fatherless child!
NDA!
The Earth is a place of call.
NDA!
Man stops here and goes on.
NDA!"

All about the Boy
in his lap
on the ground

67

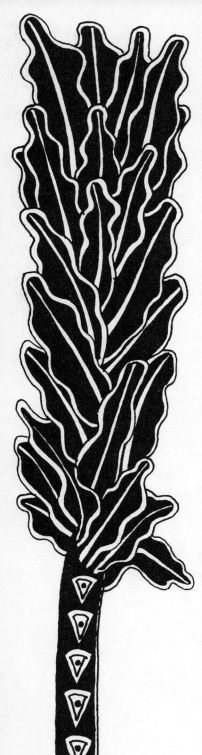

all around the tree
fell the *ripe Udala fruit*.

The Boy *ate* of the delicious Udala fruit.
Never had he been so full.
Never had he felt so contented.

In the evening the stepmother and stepbrothers
returned from the village.
They saw the tall Udala tree in their garden
and were astonished.

The Boy told them to pick whatever of the Udala
fruit they wanted
from the ground.
But he warned them *never to touch*
his magic Udala tree.
They must never *climb* the tree
or *pick* the fruit.

The stepmother and stepbrothers ate of the delicious
fruit and were delighted.

Some days later
when the Boy was hoeing the garden
he heard a noise in his tree.
The two stepbrothers had climbed the Udala tree
and were breaking the branches
to get at the fruit!

The orphan boy was FURIOUS!

He began to chant for the tree to grow
    higher into the air
carrying the two boys with it.

"Udala GROW!
NDA!
Udala GROW!!
NDA!
GROW! For motherless child!
NDA!
GROW! For fatherless child!
NDA!
The Earth is a place of call!
NDA!
Man stops here and goes on!
NDA!"

The stepbrothers began to scream for *help*.

Their mother ran from the house.
She *begged* the Orphan Boy to stop the tree.

But he was *angry*
and he *would not*.

He chanted for the tree to grow *taller*
into the sky.

"UDALA GROW!!!
NDA!
UDALA GROW!!!
NDA!
GROW!! For MOTHERLESS child!
NDA!
GROW!! For FATHERLESS child!
NDA!
The Earth is a place of call!
NDA!
Man stops here and goes on!
NDA!"

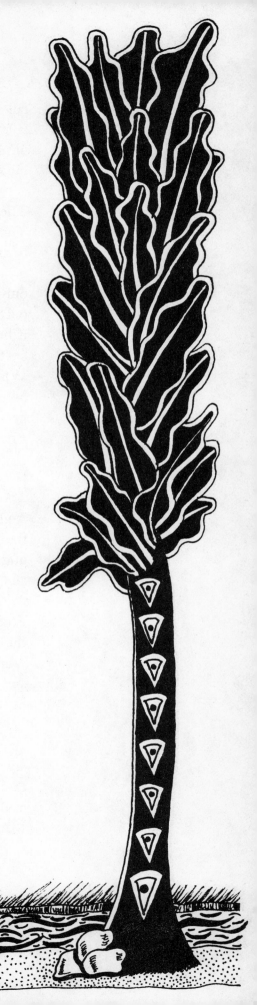

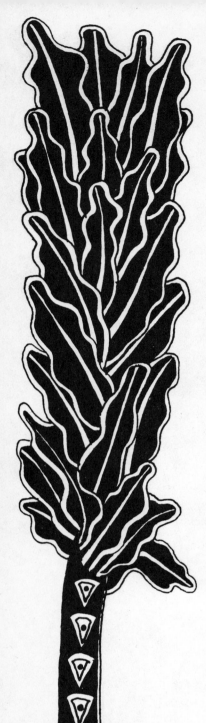

And the tree grew taller . . .
taller . . .
taller . . .
until the boys disappeared
into the clouds.

The villagers ran to see this strange thing.
Then the stepmother . . .
before all the assembled villagers . . .
promised to give the Boy
only the *best food* to eat
only the *lightest* WORK to do
if he would bring back her sons.

When the Boy heard her make this promise
before the entire village
he knew she would have to keep her promise.
And so he relented.

He called for the tree to *shrink*.

And slowly
the tree shrank back toward the earth
until it was its normal size again
and the boys were able to climb back to the ground.

From that day
the Orphan Boy
was given only the *best* food
and only the *lightest* labor
in that household.

And always . . .
always . . .
that Boy remembered to share with everyone
the fruit of his
MAGIC UDALA TREE.

70

ONE MAN'S TRASH

*a contemporary ballad
by Richard Morton*

It starts when you fill up your grocery bag
With boxes and bottles and cans
Then one day your folks start to naggedy-nag
You to take out the garbage, young man
(or la-dy!)
Take out the trash, pile it up so neat
Just like everybody else who lives on the street
A truck comes along and takes it all away
And dumps it on a mountain that gets bigger every day

(Chorus)
One man's trash is another man's treasure
It's all in the way that the eyes behold
One man's chore is another man's pleasure
And one woman's junk is another woman's gold

71

It starts when you go for a burger and fries
All wrapped up in paper and foam
Toss in a soda pop and blueberry pie
It's more fun than eating at home
You clean up the table as neat as a pin
Smoosh up all the garbage and toss it in the bin
A truck comes along and takes it all away
And dumps it on a mountain that gets bigger every day

(Chorus)
One man's trash . . .

Then one day the truck drives back to your house
And drops all the trash at your door
The dump's been closed 'cause the mountain fell down
It just couldn't take any more
I guess we let the mountain grow way too high
I wish we had another chance so we could try
To separate the garbage from the stuff that we could use
Then we wouldn't have these
"Up-to-our-neck-in-garbage
Landfills-closing-all-over-the-place
People-wanting-to-build-incinerators
In-our-own-back-yard blues!"

(Chorus)
One man's trash . . .

Jackal's Favorite
GAME

an African folk tale retold by Ashley Bryan

Children, let me tell you 'bout Jackal and Hare.
Said, "Listen while I tell a tale of Jackal and Hare.
Jackal played at friendship,
Said, 'Playing's all I care'!"

Jackal played at friendship with Hare.

Jackal never cared at all how Hare felt, uh-uh! Jackal laughed his sad Jackal laugh and cared about nothing but playing games. He had the bad habit of tackling and tickling Hare to force him to play. So whenever Jackal saw Hare coming, Jackal put him down. Uh-huh, Jackal tackled Hare to the ground.

"La-boohoo-laha," laughed Jackal. "Playing's all I care!"

"Let go!" gasped Hare as Jackal tackled him to the prickly grass.

Jackal didn't listen to Hare's cry, uh-uh! Jackal didn't care. He only played at friendship, said "Playing's all I care." Then Jackal tickled Hare as he rolled him in the prickly grass.

"Let me hee-haw up!" giggled Hare as Jackal tickled. "Stop tickling me, hee-hee!"

"La-boohoo-laha!" laughed Jackal. "La-boohoo-laha!"

Every time they met, to get the games started, Jackal tackled and tickled Hare. He never let Hare up until he agreed to play hide-and-seek. That was Jackal's favorite game and he always cried out, "Me first! Me first! You're it!"

One day Hare was out, playing all by himself. He was having a good time too, doing the Hare-Hop and singing:

"I jump high, jump higher,
Get ready, jump steady,
To the sky, yeah!"

"La-boohoo-laha, la-boohoo-laha."

"Uh-huh," said Hare. "That's Jackal's laugh. I'd better hide from that tickle-tackler."

Hare ducked behind a tree.

"Come out, come out, wherever you are!" cried Jackal. "I saw you jumping."

Hare didn't budge. He hummed to himself:

> *"Some friends are true friends,*
> *Some are makes-you-blue friends,*
> *You can tell by what they do*
> *Who is true, who makes you blue.*
> *And Jackal makes me blue."*

"La-boohoo-laha, I know you're hiding," said Jackal. "Hide-and-seek is my favorite game and playing's all I care."

"Uh-huh!" said Hare. "I won't play if you tackle and tickle me."

"I won't tickle or tackle," said Jackal, "but you know hide-and-seek is my game. Me first! Me first!"

Hare stepped out of hiding and asked, "How come you always go first?"

Jackal clapped his paws, clicked his claws, snapped his jaws and said:

> *"Because I'm bigger than you,*
> *Because I'm faster too.*
> *Because I'm tough as can be,*
> *So don't you 'How come' me!"*

Jackal's reasons didn't seem fair at all to Hare, but he didn't dare go on about it, uh-uh! Jackal went first.

Jackal spun Hare around three times.

"Now, lean against the tree and count out loud," Jackal said. "Close your eyes. No peeking!"

74

Hare closed his eyes and chanted:

> *"Cabbages, peppers, carrots and peas,*
> *Count them by ones, by twos, by threes.*
> *I'll find you first, then I'll plant these,*
> *Cabbages, peppers, carrots and peas."*

While Hare counted, Jackal skipped off and hid in a clump of bushes. He crouched low and covered himself with twigs and leaves. Jackal was sure that Hare would never find him in his bush disguise. He didn't notice that his tail stuck out. It switched back and forth as he sang:

> *"I cover myself with leaves.*
> *I close my eyes.*
> *You'll never, ever find me*
> *Till I yell, 'Surprise!' "*

Hare looked here. Hare looked there. So far, no Jackal anywhere. Hare put his hands on his hips and hopped to the bushes. He was about to hop on when he saw a tail switch.

"Uh-huh!" said Hare. "I never saw a tail-wagging bush before."

Hare walked up to the bush and called, "Come out! Come out, wherever you are. A telltale tail's told me you're in there."

Jackal didn't budge, but his tail switched on.

Hare called again, "Come out, come out wherever you are. I spy Jackal!"

Hare stamped on Jackal's tail.

"Yow!" yelled Jackal. He jumped up and the leaves and twigs fell off of him.

"Surprise! You thought I was a bush, eh! You didn't see me. I go again."

"Uh-uh!" said Hare. "I go now. I knew you were there. Your tail may be bushy, but bushes don't wag tails."

Jackal brushed that off.

75

"I said, 'I go again!' " Jackal insisted. "Remember:

> *I'm bigger than you.*
> *I'm faster, too.*
> *I'm tough as can be,*
> *So don't you 'I go' me!"*

Jackal reached out, snatched Hare and spun him around three times. "Now, count, and don't say you won't," Jackal ordered.

"Not fair," Hare murmured to himself. He didn't like being cheated out of his turn. He closed his eyes and chanted softly, so softly he could hardly be heard:

> *"Cabbages, peppers, carrots, peas.*
> *Count by ones, by twos, by threes.*
> *I'll find you, then I'll plant these:*
> *Cabbages, peppers, carrots and peas."*

Jackal scampered off to a grove of trees. He broke off some branches, then he took a vine and tied the branches around his waist.

"La-boohoo-laha," laughed Jackal. "Hiding's the best part of hide-and-seek. Now, I'm a tree. If I close my eyes, Hare won't see me."

Jackal stood up straight and still. He tucked his tail in this time, then he closed his eyes.

Hare opened his eyes. He didn't see Jackal by the home base.

"Ready or not, here I come!" Hare called.

First Hare hopped to the bush where Jackal had crouched before. He beat about the bush. No Jackal there. Hare searched the high grasses and looked behind some stones. No traces of Jackal in either of those places.

Hare ran to the grove of trees. He saw a strange sight. A tree with two legs.

"Uh-huh," said Hare:

> *"Your eyes are closed,*
> *But I can see.*
> *I spy Jackal,*
> *One, two, three!"*

Hare poked Jackal in the ribs, jaa!

"Ow!" Jackal cried. He dropped his arms and the branches. "My eyes were closed. I looked like a tree. I didn't see you. How did you see me?"

"I kept my eyes open," said Hare. "You close yours now. It's my turn. You're it."

Jackal had taken two turns and he was tempted to take three, but he relented and let Hare take a turn, too.

Now it was Hare's turn to spin Jackal around three times and to tell him, "Count out loud, I want to hear you! And close your eyes. No peeking!"

Jackal closed his eyes and leaned against a tree. He'd rather hide than seek any day. But he'd find Hare and then he'd go again, uh-huh! His count was a blues chant:

> *"Okra, cassava, coconuts and corn.*
> *Said, okra, cassava, coconuts, corn.*
> *I'll count them till I find you*
> *If it takes me all day long."*

As soon as Jackal began his chant, Hare hopped off to find a good hiding place. Bippity-bop-bop, he hopped, bippity-bop-bop. He looked back to see if Jackal was peeking. Paa-lam! Hare tripped over a tree root and fell into a hole. The hole was deep enough to keep Hare well hidden from sight.

"Eh, eh!" said Hare. "What luck! I couldn't have chosen a better hiding place."

Hare made himself at home in the hole. He leaned back and stared up at the tree branches and the sky. He enjoyed watching the butterflies and birds that flew by while he waited.

Jackal finished his hide-and-seek count and set out to find Hare. He poked about in a clump of bushes and called, "Come out, come out wherever you are!"

Hare heard the loud call from wherever Jackal looked. He didn't plan to come out of his hiding hole.

Jackal came closer. Hare didn't move or make a sound. He opened his eyes wide and looked up.

Jackal saw the holes by the tree roots and he began to look into them.

Hare heard Jackal's steps coming closer and closer. He knew he would soon be discovered, but Hare was a good hide-and-seek player. He wouldn't give up until he'd been caught.

"I see you. I see you!" Jackal cried each time he looked into a dark hole. But he hadn't seen Hare yet.

"You may have seen a spider,
You may have seen a bee,
You may have seen a cricket,
But you haven't seen me."

Just then Jackal came to the hole in which Hare was hiding. Jackal looked straight into two large eyes that stared up at him out of the dark. Hare knew he'd been caught.

"Aie yaie! Aie yaie!" yelled Jackal.

He tumbled over backwards and almost caught his foot in a hole. He got to his feet and fled.

"Eh, eh!" said Hare. "What is this? Jackal found me, yet he's running away. That's no way to play hide-and-seek."

"Aie yaie! Aie yaie!" Jackal cried as he ran. "I have seen the Big-Eyed Monster. The Big-Eyed Monster is after me!"

Hare hopped out of his hole and heard Jackal's cry.

"So that's why he fled. He thinks I'm a big-eyed monster."

Hare laughed and took off after Jackal, bippity-bop-bop, bippity-bop-hop.

"Here comes the Big-Eyed Monster," Hare called. "Here comes Hare, the Big-Eyed Monster!"

"Aie yaie! Aie yaie!" Jackal wailed. "Only a monster has eyes like that! Its head must be huge. Its body, big and brutal, I bet!"

Jackal was so frightened that he didn't look where he was running. His feet caught in a vine and tripped him up. Down he went, flam!

Jackal lay there crying and panting and kicking. He couldn't untangle the vine from his feet. He closed his eyes in fright.

"The Big-Eyed Monster will get me," he cried. "La-boohoo, la-boohoo."

Hare caught up with Jackal and loosened the vine from around his feet. Jackal kept his eyes shut.

"O Big-Eyed Monster," he cried. "La-boohoo, la-boohoo! I'll do whatever you ask. Don't eat me!"

Hare sang:

"Because I'm bigger than you,
Because I'm faster, too,
Because I'm tough as can be,
So don't you 'Don't eat me!'"

Jackal opened his eyes.

"La-boohoo-lala, Brother Hare!!" Jackal cried, "Save me! This hide-and-seek game is for real. The Big-Eyed Monster is after me."

"Don't be silly," said Hare. "Look at me!"

Hare shaded his face and opened his eyes wide.

"You, Brother Hare!" Jackal exclaimed. "You're the Big-Eyed Monster!"

"Uh-huh," said Hare. "You found me, but then you ran away bawling. That's no way to play hide-and-seek."

"You scared me," said Jackal. "You shouldn't hide in dark holes and open your eyes so big and wide, not when we play hide-and-seek. Uh-uh! That's my favorite game. Promise not to do it anymore."

"You said you'd do whatever I ask when I loosened the vine from your feet," said Hare. "Promise not to tackle and tickle me anymore."

Jackal and Hare exchanged promises right then and there, and they kept them. Uh-huh they did. Jackal stopped playing friendship with Hare and became a true friend.

After that, when Jackal and Hare played games, Jackal often said: "You first, Brother Hare. You first."

Now that's true friendship, isn't it? Uh huh!
And playing's all I care!

FROG AND LOCUST

a Pueblo tale from the Southwestern United States retold by Joe Hayes

Once it didn't rain for a whole year. The grass turned brown and died. Trees and bushes lost their leaves. In the canyon bottom, where a lively stream usually flowed, there were just a few puddles of water left. And every day those puddles got smaller and smaller.

Living at the edge of one puddle was a frog. The frog saw his puddle get smaller with each passing day, and he knew that if it didn't rain the puddle would soon dry up. And he would die!

But the frog knew how to sing a rain song. So he sang to see if he could bring some rain. The frog croaked—

R-R-RAIN, R-R-RAIN, R-R-RAIN . . .

But his song wasn't loud enough to reach the top of the mountain, and that is where the Rain God lived. The Rain God couldn't hear the frog singing, and no rain came.

Not far from the frog's puddle was a bush, and living in the bush was a locust. The locust knew that if it didn't rain, he wouldn't live through the summer. So as he clung to the bush the locust buzzed—

R-r-r-rain-n-n-n, r-r-r-rain-n-n-n . . .

But that song wasn't loud enough to reach the top of the mountain either. And when the locust saw that there were no clouds in the sky, and it wasn't going to rain, he started to cry—

Ee-he-he-he-he . . .

The frog heard someone crying, so he hopped over there. He looked up and croaked—

WHAT'S THE MATTER-R-R ..?
WHAT'S THE MATTER-R-R ..?

80

The locust told him, "If it doesn't rain, I'm going to die!"

When the frog heard that, he thought about how the same thing would happen to him if it didn't rain, and he started to cry too—

WAH-WAH-WAH . . .

But then the locust got an idea. He thought—when one person works all alone, he doesn't get much done. But when people work together, they can do a lot of work. So the locust said, "Frog, maybe we should sing together."

The frog thought that was a good idea. So they added their songs together—

R-R-RAIN . . . r-r-r-rain-n-n . . .

R-R-RAIN . . . r-r-r-rain-n-n . . .

It still wasn't loud enough to go to the top of the mountain. But it was loud enough to go to the next puddle up the canyon. And living over there was another frog. On the other side of the canyon, there were even more frogs. They heard the frog sing and thought they would join in and sing along with him. They all sang—

R-R-RAIN, R-R-RAIN, R-R-RAIN . . .

In the nearby bushes, and in the bunches of grass still growing at the puddle's edge, there were also more locusts. They heard the song and thought they'd join in too—

R-r-r-rain-n-n, r-r-rain-n-n . . .

Soon all the frogs and locusts were singing—

R-R-RAIN . . . r-r-r-rain-n-n . . .

R-R-RAIN . . . r-r-r-rain-n-n . . .

It was a loud song! It went clear to the top of the mountain!

The Rain God heard the song. He climbed up to the center of the sky and gathered dark clouds all around him. From the distant mountains he made the cool wind begin to blow. Rain drops started falling. The rain fell faster . . . and faster. It was a big storm!

The canyon stream filled back up with water. The trees and bushes got new leaves. The whole land came to life again. And it was all because the frogs and locusts worked together!

And that's why it is to this day that if one person's fields are dry and dying, he doesn't go off by himself and sing for rain. But all the people gather together. They dance with one heart, and with one voice they sing. And in that way they can always bring the rain.

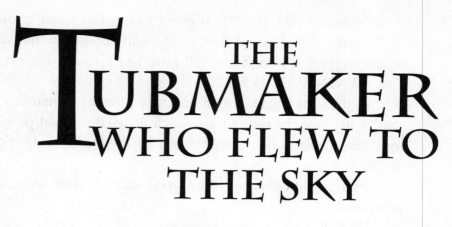

THE TUBMAKER WHO FLEW TO THE SKY

a Japanese folk tale retold by Yoshiko Uchida

Long, long ago, there lived in Japan a man who earned his living by making tubs and barrels. He made great wide tubs for baths, he made tall high barrels for wine, and he made short squat tubs for soy sauce. He worked hard from morning till night, and the sound of hammering and pounding always filled the air around his shop.

One day, a wine merchant hurried into his shop and called out to him, "Make me three large barrels by tomorrow morning." And then, before the tubmaker could tell him how busy he was, he ran out of the shop and disappeared down the street.

The tubmaker shook his head and hurried outside behind his shop. There, in his small yard, he began to fit the barrel staves together, hammering and pounding until his arms ached. When, at last, he was fitting the hoops around the last barrel, a strange thing happened. The hoop suddenly snapped with a WHANNNNNG, and caught the tubmaker by the sleeves. Before he knew what was happening, he was swept into the air with a swoosh, and was sailing up into the sky.

"Whhhat's happening? Where am I?" the tubmaker muttered to himself. He was flying up, up, and up, higher and higher still, until soon he was soaring into the clouds.

82

Suddenly, he stopped, and when he looked around, he discovered he had landed right in the middle of a big gray cloud. When he finally caught his breath and looked up, he saw the great god of thunder standing in front of him.

"Well, well," the thunder god roared. "What have we here?" He bent down to look at the tubmaker who sat with his legs crossed on the gray softness of the cloud. The tubmaker felt the cold icy breath of the thunder god as he bent down to inspect him, and he was filled with a great and terrible fear.

"I . . . I . . . I . . ." he began, but his teeth chattered so, he could not talk.

"Well, well! Out with it," said the thunder god. "What are you trying to tell me?"

And so the tubmaker took a deep breath and began again. "I . . . I . . . I've come from Japan . . . down below. . . . I was fitting the hoop on a wine barrel, when suddenly, before I knew what was happening, I was sailing up into the sky."

The tubmaker shook his head. He still couldn't believe what had happened. "It was very strange," he said wonderingly. "Very strange indeed. A hoop has never snapped like that before."

The tubmaker looked sad and forlorn, but the thunder god laughed with a great thunderous roar. "HA, HA, HA! You must have been a funny sight," he said. "I've seen birds flying this high, but I've never seen a human being up here before."

Then the god suddenly seemed to remember what he was doing. "You've come just in time," he said. "I've been meaning to send some rain down below for a long time, but my assistant who carries my water sacks has disappeared. I was just looking for someone to help me."

The tubmaker looked around, but no assistant rainmaker was in sight. He looked up and saw that the thunder god was looking right at him. "Do you mean you'd like me to help?" he asked timidly.

"You're a trifle small," the thunder god said, "but I think you'll do."

Then he handed the tubmaker an enormous sack filled with water, and standing very straight and tall, he began to beat on his eight great drums.

"WHANNG ... CRASH ... BANG ... BOOM!" The drums roared and rumbled and sounded like a thousand lions about to eat him up. The tubmaker held his hands over his ears and closed his eyes tight. But soon, he heard the thunder god calling to him.

"Now, let the rain fall!" he roared.

So, the tubmaker opened his eyes, raised the sack, and began to pour water on the earth below. Soon, thunder roared, lightning flashed, and great torrents of water went rushing down from the great gray clouds.

"Keep pouring! Keep pouring!" shouted the thunder god, and he handed the tubmaker one sack of water after the other.

As the tubmaker looked down, he could see everything that was going on below. People were rushing and scurrying and running for cover. "What a terrible storm!" they shouted, as they ran this way and that.

Watching from the sky, the tubmaker laughed as he saw the commotion he had caused. Here was a woman dropping her laundry as she hurried to take it off the long bamboo poles. Over there was a farmer running home from the fields, holding a straw cape over his head. He slipped and stumbled as he ran on the wet road, and was covered with mud from head to toe.

"My, those little people look funny," thought the tubmaker. And he was having such a good time, he wished he could always live high above the earth and watch the tiny people below. He was so busy looking down, he scarcely paid any attention to what he was doing. He hopped merrily from cloud to cloud, whistling and singing, and letting the water pour out from the big sacks of rain.

"Have some rain, little people," he sang. "Have some rain!"

Suddenly, just as he was hopping from one cloud to the next, his foot slipped. Still clutching one of the big sacks of rain, the tubmaker felt himself falling off the cloud.

"Help!" he shouted to the thunder god, but by the time the god turned around, it was too late. His assistant had already zoomed down through the gray skies and fallen to earth.

"I hope I land in a nice soft rice paddy," he thought. But when he finally stopped and opened his eyes, he found he had landed right on top of a very tall tree growing in the yard of the village temple. The tubmaker peered down cautiously. The ground was covered with puddles that his rain had made. He wanted to call for help, but the yard was quiet and empty, and not a single priest was in sight. The tubmaker sat in the tree and waited for a long time. Soon, it grew cold, and he began to shiver as the wind began to blow.

"Help!" he shouted. "Help!" But he was so far up, no one could hear him. A few birds flew by and looked at him curiously, but they were no help to him at all.

"I wonder if I will have to stay here forever," thought the tubmaker gloomily. "I would give anything to be back down on the ground again."

As he sat wondering what to do, he saw a priest walking slowly through the yard. "Help!" he shouted in his loudest, strongest voice. The priest thought he heard someone calling, and he looked to the left and he looked to the right. Still, he couldn't see a soul.

"Up here!" shouted the tubmaker. "I'm up here!"

"The voice seems to be coming from the tree top," said the priest. He was old and he could not see very well. He squinted through his glasses and at last saw the tubmaker waving frantically from the highest limb of the ginkgo tree.

"Ah . . . ah . . ." said the old priest. "What are you doing up there? Come down at once! It's dangerous to be up so high."

"I know it's dangerous," shouted the tubmaker. "I want to come down, but I can't. Help me!"

The old priest scratched his head. "Wait!" he called. "I'll go for help."

Soon all the priests of the temple came out and looked up at the tubmaker perched like a big black crow on the highest limb of their ginkgo tree.

"Hmmmm, how very strange," they said. "I wonder how he ever got up there."

The tubmaker watched them as they clustered in a little circle and wondered how to get him down. "If we only had a ladder," they said. "But there is no ladder that will reach quite that high."

85

At last the priests seemed to have thought of something, and they ran back into the temple.

"Come back! Don't leave me up here!" the tubmaker shouted.

Soon they were back with a big blanket which they stretched out beneath the tree. Holding on to its edges, they called to the tubmaker, "Jump! We'll catch you!"

Now the blanket looked terribly small and terribly far away, but the tubmaker decided he would either have to jump or stay in the tree for the rest of his life.

"All right," he called in a small weak voice. "I'll jump."

He took a deep breath, closed his eyes, and took a big leap. PLOP and PLUNK . . . He landed right in the middle of the blanket, bouncing like a rubber ball.

"How good it is to be back on earth!" the tubmaker said gratefully, and bowing low, he thanked each of the priests who had caught him in the blanket. Then he hurried home to his shop where the barrels and tubs still waited for him.

"My, it's good to be back," he thought happily. He looked up to see if he could see the great thunder god peering down at him from one of the clouds, but all he could see was the clear night sky covered with thousands of stars that seemed to be laughing at him.

The tubmaker wondered if it was all a dream, for there wasn't a single rain cloud in the whole night sky. He looked around his shop, and then he looked at the barrels he had been working on that morning. Yes, there was the broken hoop that had sent him into the sky. And, yes, the barrels were filled with the very rain he had poured down from the gray cloud.

The tubmaker smiled as he thought of his strange adventure. He picked up his hammer and repaired the broken hoop of his wine barrel so it would be ready for the wine merchant in the morning. But this time, he was very, very careful not to get his sleeve caught again.

It was great fun helping the thunder god, but it was even better being down on earth in his own little shop. And from that day on, the tubmaker was careful to keep both feet planted firmly on the ground.

WHEN THE RAIN CAME UP FROM CHINA

a Paul Bunyan tall tale retold by Dell J. McCormick

The year Paul Bunyan came west he had a big camp near the mouth of the Columbia River. It was probably the biggest logging camp the West Coast ever knew. The bunkhouses stretched for miles in all directions and each had five tiers of bunks, one above the other.

The dining room was a problem with so many men to feed. Ole built a giant soup kettle that covered five and a half acres and sent for a Mississippi stern-wheeler. It was quite a sight with the fire burning merrily under it and the old steamer paddling around mixing up vegetable soup for dinner. One day a team of oxen fell in but it didn't worry Sourdough Sam any. He just changed the menu to "beef broth" that night and everybody seemed mighty pleased with the result.

The waiters wore roller skates, but the tables were so long they used to wear out two and three pair of skates just making the rounds with hot coffee. Tiny Tim the Chore Boy drove the salt and pepper wagon. He usually drove the length of the table and stayed all night at the far end, driving back to the kitchen in the morning for a fresh load. It took so much time getting all the men into the dining room some of them almost starved to death waiting their turn. Paul finally had to build lunch counters outside where the men waiting in line could get a light lunch in the meantime.

Paul expected a wet damp winter in the Douglas fir country, but month after month went by and never a sign of rain. He had all the bunkhouse roofs lined with thick tar paper to keep out the rain. The men were given rainproof slickers to put on over their mackinaws, and Babe the Blue Ox had a big tarpaulin for his own use. It was made from the canvas of Barnum and Bailey's main tent and fitted him fine except that it was a little short around the knees.

Just when they least expected it, however, it began to rain, and it was the strangest rain that anyone ever saw! Instead of raining down it rained up! The earth fairly spouted water. It filled the men's boots. It rained up their sleeves. It went up their pant legs in spite of everything they could do. It was impossible to escape! Naturally the rain coats and the tarpaulins and the tar roofs on the bunkhouses were useless, for the rain was coming up from below.

It seeped through the bunkhouse floors and flooded the cook shanty. Men crawled into the top bunks to escape and floated from one bunk to another on homemade rafts. Hot Biscuit Slim and Sourdough Sam cooked the evening meal floating around the kitchen on flour barrels. Cream Puff Fatty sat in an empty tub and paddled back and forth to the stove cooking apple pies.

Johnnie Inkslinger looked at the rain coming up from the ground and cried in great surprise:

"It's raining from China!"

Up from China came the bubbling rain until the whole forest was one vast swamp. Little fountains of water sprang up everywhere. It rained in the men's faces when they bent over to pick up a cant hook or peavey. It spurted up their coatsleeves and ran down their backs inside their heavy mackinaws. A knothole in the bunkhouse floor started a geyser of water ten feet high. Paul decided to turn the bunkhouses upside down so the tar paper roofs would keep the water out. By that time the water was well up to his ankles, which meant that it would come up to the armpit of the average man.

Just as Paul had about decided to abandon the camp, the rain from China stopped as quickly as it began. The water seeped back into the moist earth, and by nightfall most of the water had disappeared except in pools here and there throughout the woods. Paul breathed a sigh of relief to find his feet on solid ground again, and the men built huge campfires to dry out their soaked clothing.

It was many years, however, before the lumberjacks in Paul's camp forgot their terrible experience with the rain that came from China. Even now when some camp orator starts to tell about a terrific rainstorm an old-timer will shake his head slowly and remark:

"Stranger, you don't even know what rain is unless you was with Paul Bunyan out in Oregon. You ain't never seen rain nor got wet unless you was working with Paul Bunyan out west the year the rain came up from China!"

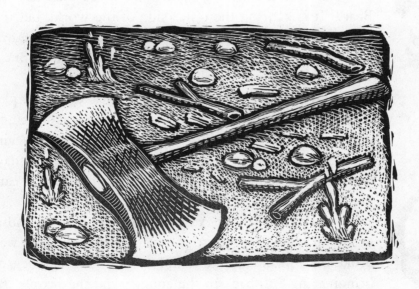

How Grandmother Spider Stole the Sun

a Muskogee (Creek) legend from Oklahoma
told by Joseph Bruchac

When the Earth was first made, there was no light. It was very hard for the animals and the people in the darkness. Finally the animals decided to do something about it.

"I have heard there is something called the Sun," said the Bear. "It is kept on the other side of the world, but the people there will not share it. Perhaps we can steal a piece of it."

All the animals agreed that it was a good idea. But who would be the one to steal the Sun?

The Fox was the first to try. He sneaked to the place where the Sun was kept. He waited until no one was looking. Then he grabbed a piece of it in his mouth and ran. But the Sun was so hot it burned his mouth and he dropped it. To this day all foxes have black mouths because that first fox burned his carrying the Sun.

The Possum tried next. In those days Possum had a very bushy tail. She crept up to the place where the Sun was kept, broke off a piece and hid it in her tail. Then she began to run, bringing the Sun back to the animals and the people. But the Sun was so hot it burned off all the hair on her tail and she lost hold of it. To this day all possums have bare tails because the Sun burned away the hair on that first possum.

90

Then Grandmother Spider tried. Instead of trying to hold the Sun herself, she wove a bag out of her webbing. She put the piece of the Sun into her bag and carried it back with her. Now the question was where to put the Sun.

Grandmother Spider told them, "The Sun should be up high in the sky. Then everyone will be able to see it and benefit from its light."

All the animals agreed, but none of them could reach up high enough. Even if they carried it to the top of the tallest tree, that would not be high enough for everyone on the Earth to see the Sun. Then they decided to have one of the birds carry the Sun up to the top of the sky. Everyone knew the Buzzard could fly the highest, so he was chosen.

Buzzard placed the Sun on top of his head, where his feathers were the thickest, for the Sun was still very hot, even inside Grandmother Spider's bag. He began to fly, up and up toward the top of the sky. As he flew the Sun grew hotter. Up and up he went, higher and higher, and the Sun grew hotter and hotter still. Now the Sun was burning through Grandmother Spider's bag, but the Buzzard still kept flying up toward the top of the sky. Up and up he went and the Sun grew hotter. Now it was burning away the feathers on top of his head, but he continued on. Now all of his feathers were gone, but he flew higher. Now it was turning the bare skin of his head all red, but he continued to fly. He flew until he reached the top of the sky, and there he placed the Sun where it would give light to everyone.

Because he carried the Sun up to the top of the sky, Buzzard was honored by all the birds and animals. Though his head is naked and ugly because he was burned carrying the Sun, he is still the highest flyer of all, and he can be seen circling the Sun to this day. And because Grandmother Spider brought the Sun in her bag of webbing, at times the Sun makes rays across the sky which are shaped like the rays in Grandmother Spider's web. It reminds everyone that we are all connected, like the strands of Grandmother Spider's web, and it reminds everyone of what Grandmother Spider did for all the animals and the people.

How Wolf Helped
THE SAMI

*a Sami tale from Lapland retold
by Ken Jackson (Grey Eagle)*

Long ago, when the Sami were first trying to catch and herd the wild reindeer, they needed help. The reindeer were nervous and swift in flight and it was not possible to round them up and keep them in permanent herds. And yet the Sami knew it had to be done. They needed reindeer skins for clothing to keep them warm in the harsh winters, reindeer meat to keep them fed, and reindeer milk for butter and cheese.

Since there weren't enough Sami to catch and herd the reindeer, it was decided to ask the animal people for help. The most respected Sami, the Shaman, was asked to go among the animals to request help.

The first animal he met was Hare, who was stretched out on a sun-warmed rock. The Shaman spoke to him politely, "You who are so swift of foot, will you help us round up the reindeer?"

Hare yawned and replied, "No, I can't help you just now. I'm thinking of building myself a home for the winter."

The Shaman was angered by Hare's selfish reply. "Lazy lout!" he shouted. "You can sit there and think about building a home, but that's as far as you'll ever get. You'll only think about building and never get it done."

And so it is today. Hare lounges about in the warm summer thinking about building a home but never gets it done. When winter comes, Hare must live without shelter, outside in the cold and snow.

The next animal the Shaman met was Bear, who sat yawning and scratching himself. The Shaman spoke to him politely, "You who are the strongest, most feared animal in the forest and on the tundra, will you help us round up the reindeer?"

Bear yawned and replied, "No, I can't help you just now. I'm sleepy, so sleepy. I'm going to take a long nap."

The Shaman was angered by Bear's selfish reply. "Lazy lout!" he shouted. "You can have your nap. You and those who come after you will be so tired that you will sleep the whole winter through."

And so it is today. Bear goes to sleep in the fall and doesn't wake up again until spring. Bear sleeps through the whole winter.

The Shaman next met Wolf, resting by the side of a field. The Shaman spoke to him politely, "You who are most admired for the way you help one another, will you help us round up the reindeer?"

"That would be fun," Wolf replied. "We can do it together, as a pack. That way, none of us will have to work too hard and get too tired."

And so Wolf and his pack helped the Sami, rounding up the reindeer and then keeping the reindeer herd from scattering. When one wolf sat down to rest, another would take up the duties.

The Sami watched the wolves and learned many things. The wolves worked in teams and taught the Sami to do the same, in hunting, herding, and child-rearing. The wolves also cooperated in helping the ill and elderly. And they got food not just for themselves but also for those unable to hunt on their own.

The Shaman was impressed with all these wolf ways which helped the Sami and taught them lessons. "You have my blessing," he said. "You can have a snug, warm home when the weather is cold and you can continue to hunt throughout the winter."

And so it is today. Unlike Hare, Wolf has a snug home to live in during the cold winter. Unlike Bear, Wolf is awake during the winter months and goes out to hunt when tracks are easy to find.

But the wolves told the Sami that they would be bored just being reindeer herders. They needed to run free, to try new things, to visit new places. So they trained their cousins, the dogs, to herd the reindeer. Dogs do that duty even today. And the Sami reward them well, keeping them fed and allowing them into their tents when it is cold or wet outside.

When the dogs hear the wolves howl, they answer them, thanking their cousins for helping bring them such good lives as reindeer herders. But the wolves know that it is they who have the best life, since they can run free.

And the Sami honor the wolf for all its help and for the many lessons taught by retelling this story.

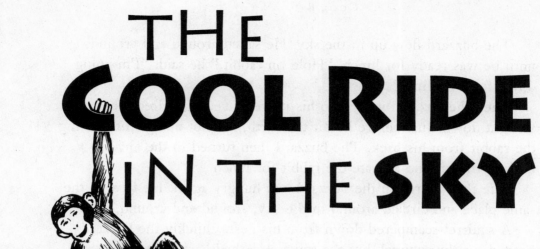

THE COOL RIDE IN THE SKY

a black American folk tale
told by Diane Wolkstein

It was a very hot summer day.

All the animals were hiding from the sun under bushes or in their holes, but not the buzzard. He was sailing around in the sky looking for food.

He'd been sailing around for hours, when suddenly—

A rabbit hopped out of his hole. The buzzard quickly spotted him and swooped down, but the rabbit hopped back in his hole.

The buzzard landed beside the rabbit's hole.

"Hello rabbit," said the buzzard sweetly. "How is it down in your hole?"

"Hot!" cried the rabbit. "It's hot in my house and it's hot on the ground. How is it up in the sky?"

"Oh rabbit," said the buzzard. "It's as cool as can be. Why don't you jump on my back and I'll take you up there?"

The rabbit peeked out of his hole. The sun was blazing hot.

"Hurry rabbit," said the buzzard. "I don't have time to be giving free rides to everyone."

The rabbit looked at the buzzard. The buzzard looked so cool and pleased that the rabbit decided to take a chance.

"Okay," he said, and hopped onto the buzzard's back.

The buzzard flew up in the sky. He sailed around and around, until he was ready for lunch. "Hold on rabbit," he said. "I'm going down for a landing."

Then the buzzard went into his power dive, a hundred feet straight down. Just before he hit the earth, he shot up again throwing the rabbit from his back. The buzzard then turned in the air, flew back to the ground and ate the rabbit for lunch.

Late that afternoon the buzzard was hungry again. He flew to the same place and circled around in the sky, around and around, until—

A squirrel scampered down from his nest. Quickly the buzzard headed for the squirrel, but the squirrel dashed back into a hole in the tree.

The buzzard landed on one of the branches.

"Hello squirrel!" the buzzard called. "How are you feeling today?"

"I'm hot, buzzard. It's been hot all day and I'm still hot."

"It's cool in the sky, squirrel. Jump on my back and I'll take you up there."

Now the squirrel *knew* the buzzard was a tricky animal, but he also knew that the higher in a tree you go, the cooler it is, still—

"Jump on my back," said the buzzard, "or maybe you're afraid to fly so high?"

"Of course not!" said the squirrel. He jumped onto the buzzard's back and up they flew.

Meanwhile, a monkey who was sitting in the branches of a nearby tree had been watching the buzzard. He'd seen the trick the buzzard had played on the rabbit, and now he was watching to see what the buzzard would do with the squirrel.

The buzzard sailed around and around.

After a while the buzzard turned to the squirrel and said: "Hold on, squirrel. I'm going down for a landing."

Again the buzzard went into his power dive, a hundred feet straight down, shooting up again at the last minute, throwing the poor squirrel off his back. Then the buzzard turned, flew back and ate the squirrel for dinner.

After the buzzard had flown off, the monkey began to swing on his branch. Back and forth, back and forth until—he got an idea.

The next day it was hot again. The sun was shining brightly, and the animals were hiding from the sun. But the monkey was standing in plain sight watching the sky.

When the other animals saw the monkey standing hour after hour in the hot sun, they became more and more curious and poked their heads further out of their hiding places.

Towards noon, the monkey spotted the buzzard. He began to dance up and down, flapping his arms in the air. In less than a minute the buzzard was down on the ground beside the monkey.

"Hello monkey," he said. "What kind of dance were you doing?"

"A flying dance. Did you like it?"

"Well . . . yes—"

"Yes," said the monkey. "I was doing a flying dance, just *wishing* I could go for a cool ride in the sky."

"Oh-h monkey!" The buzzard's face broke into a great big grin. "There's nothing I like more than giving free rides in the sky. Quick, jump on my back and up we go."

The monkey winked at the other animals and slowly seated himself on the buzzard's back.

The buzzard took off. He circled around once in the sky. Then he turned to the monkey and said: "Hold on monkey, I'm going down for a landing."

"HOLD ON!" the monkey shouted back. "THERE'S GOING TO BE NO MONKEY DINNER TONIGHT!"

And the monkey whipped his tail out and wrapped it so tight around the buzzard's neck that the buzzard's eyes nearly popped out of his head.

"BUZZARD!" said the monkey, "YOU STRAIGHTEN UP AND FLY RIGHT!"

The buzzard was caught and had to fly straight on.

The monkey ordered the buzzard to fly low, so he could wave to his friends on the ground. They cheered and waved back.

"Now then buzzard," said the monkey, "up we go." And the buzzard flew up again in the cool air and sailed around in the sky, until—

The *monkey* was ready to go down. The monkey loosened his hold ever so slightly on the buzzard's neck, and the buzzard glided down to a soft landing.

All the animals crowded around the monkey laughing and cheering, while the buzzard flew off in shame.

"We won't be seeing that buzzard again for a long time," said the monkey.

Then he flapped his arms in the air and began to hop from foot to foot. He was doing the flying dance.

And soon all the animals joined him.

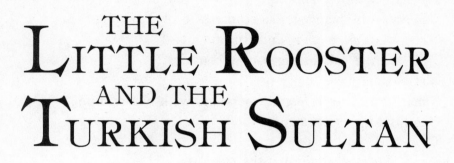

The Little Rooster and the Turkish Sultan

*a Hungarian folk tale retold
by Margaret Read MacDonald*

Some where . . .
some place . . .
across the Seven Seas . . .
There lived a Little Old Lady
and her Little Pet Rooster.

One day
the Little Rooster went out into the yard
to peck out something to eat.
He pecked and he pecked and he pecked
and he pecked out
a *diamond button!*

> "COCK-A-DOODLE-DOOOO!"
>   said the Little Rooster.
> "I *like* diamond buttons!
> I'll take this home to my good mistress.
> *She* likes diamond buttons *too!*"

He picked the diamond button up in his beak
and started to walk home.

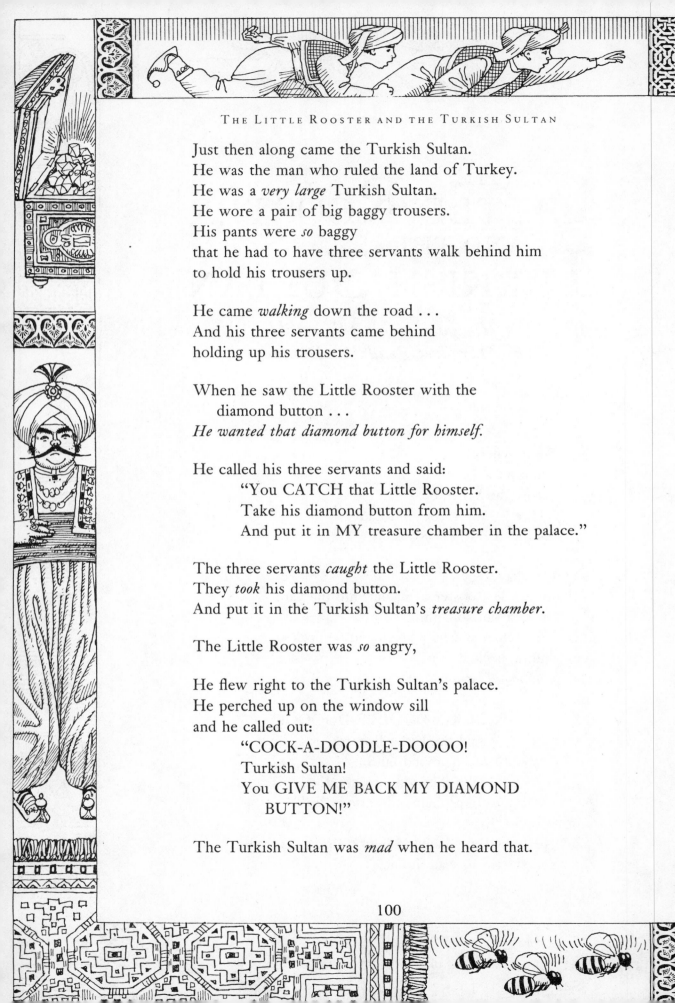

Just then along came the Turkish Sultan.
He was the man who ruled the land of Turkey.
He was a *very large* Turkish Sultan.
He wore a pair of big baggy trousers.
His pants were *so* baggy
that he had to have three servants walk behind him
to hold his trousers up.

He came *walking* down the road . . .
And his three servants came behind
holding up his trousers.

When he saw the Little Rooster with the
    diamond button . . .
He wanted that diamond button for himself.

He called his three servants and said:
    "You CATCH that Little Rooster.
    Take his diamond button from him.
    And put it in MY treasure chamber in the palace."

The three servants *caught* the Little Rooster.
They *took* his diamond button.
And put it in the Turkish Sultan's *treasure chamber*.

The Little Rooster was *so* angry,

He flew right to the Turkish Sultan's palace.
He perched up on the window sill
and he called out:
    "COCK-A-DOODLE-DOOOO!
    Turkish Sultan!
    You GIVE ME BACK MY DIAMOND
        BUTTON!"

The Turkish Sultan was *mad* when he heard that.

He called his three servants and said:
> "You CATCH that Little Rooster.
> Throw him into a WELL FULL OF WATER.
> And that will be the end of HIM."

The three servants caught the Little Rooster
and threw him into a *well full of water*.

But the Little Rooster
had a
magic stomach.

As soon as he was in the well he called out:
> "Come my Empty Stomach . . .
> Come my Empty Stomach . . .
> Drink up ALL the water in this well."

His stomach began to drink.
He *drank* and *drank* and *drank* . . .
He drank up *all* the water in that well.

He got *very* big
But he didn't drown!

Instead
He flew right back to the Turkish Sultan's palace.
He perched on the window sill.
And he called out:
> "COCK-A-DOODLE-DOOOOO!
> Turkish Sultan!
> You GIVE ME BACK MY DIAMOND
>   BUTTON!"

The Turkish Sultan was *angry* when he heard that.
He called his three servants and said:

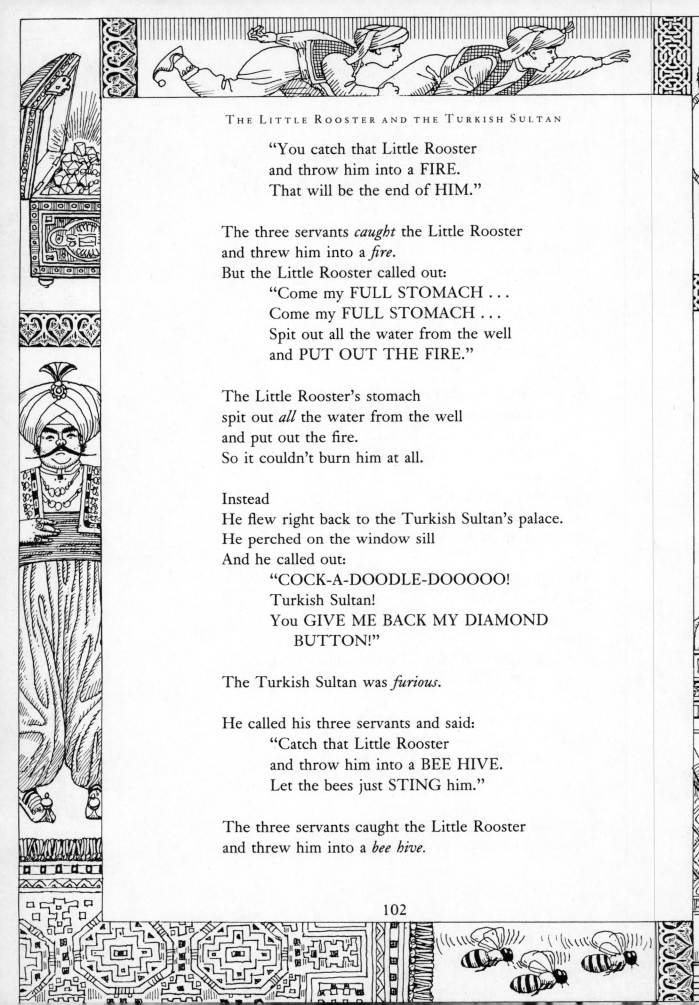

> "You catch that Little Rooster
> and throw him into a FIRE.
> That will be the end of HIM."

The three servants *caught* the Little Rooster
and threw him into a *fire*.
But the Little Rooster called out:
> "Come my FULL STOMACH . . .
> Come my FULL STOMACH . . .
> Spit out all the water from the well
> and PUT OUT THE FIRE."

The Little Rooster's stomach
spit out *all* the water from the well
and put out the fire.
So it couldn't burn him at all.

Instead
He flew right back to the Turkish Sultan's palace.
He perched on the window sill
And he called out:
> "COCK-A-DOODLE-DOOOOO!
> Turkish Sultan!
> You GIVE ME BACK MY DIAMOND
>   BUTTON!"

The Turkish Sultan was *furious*.

He called his three servants and said:
> "Catch that Little Rooster
> and throw him into a BEE HIVE.
> Let the bees just STING him."

The three servants caught the Little Rooster
and threw him into a *bee hive*.

But the Little Rooster called out:
>"Come my EMPTY STOMACH . . .
>Come my EMPTY STOMACH . . .
>Eat up ALL THE BEES IN THE BEE HIVE!"

His stomach ate up
All the bees in the bee hive.

They buzzed around inside
But they couldn't sting his magic stomach.

Instead
The Little Rooster flew right back to the
>Turkish Sultan's palace.

He perched on the window sill
And he called out:
>"COCK-A-DOODLE-DOOOOO!
>Turkish Sultan!
>You GIVE ME BACK MY DIAMOND
>>BUTTON!"

The Turkish Sultan was *infuriated.*

He called his three servants and said:
>"You catch that Little Rooster
>>and bring him to ME.
>What will I DO with him?"

The first servant said:
>"If *I* were you I would CHOP his head off."

The second servant said:
>"If *I* were you I would HANG HIM
>>from the highest tree."

But the *third* servant said:
> "If *I* were you, I know what *I* would do with him!
> I would SIT ON HIM AND SQUASH HIM!"

This was a very good idea
because the Turkish Sultan was a *very heavy*
   Turkish Sultan.

He said:
> "CATCH that Little Rooster.
> DROP him into the big bag
>   on my baggy pants behind
> and ... *let* ... *me* ... SIT ... *on him*
> *and* SQUASH *him!*"

So they caught the Little Rooster
and dropped him into the big bag
on the Turkish Sultan's baggy pants.

But the Little Rooster called out:
> "Come my FULL STOMACH
> Come my FULL STOMACH
> Let out all the BEES!
> and STING that Turkish Sultan!"

The Little Rooster's stomach let out all the *bees*.

Did they *sting* that Turkish Sultan????!!!!

> "Oh OH!!
> OW OW!!
> OOO OOO!!"

The Turkish Sultan was jumping around his throne room.

He cried:
> "Catch that Little Rooster.
> Take him to my treasure chamber

and let him HAVE his old diamond button.
I never want to SEE HIM again."

They took the Little Rooster
    to the Turkish Sultan's treasure chamber.

They said:
        "TAKE your diamond button
        and GO ALONG HOME."

They left him *all alone*
in the Turkish Sultan's treasure chamber.
The Little Rooster *looked around*.
He saw all the *diamonds*
all the *gold and silver*
all the *emeralds and rubies*
in the Turkish Sultan's treasure chamber.

So he called out:
        "Come my EMPTY STOMACH
        Come my EMPTY STOMACH
        Eat up ALL the TREASURE
        in the Turkish Sultan's treasure chamber."

His stomach
ate up all the gold and silver
all the emeralds and rubies
all the *diamonds*
in the Turkish Sultan's treasure chamber.

And when he was *very* full . . .
He waddled along home
and gave it all to his good mistress.

And they lived richly
and happily
ever after.

THE NAME OF THE TREE

A Bantu folk tale retold
by Celia Barker Lottridge

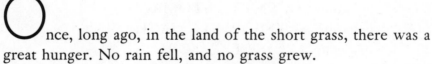

Once, long ago, in the land of the short grass, there was a great hunger. No rain fell, and no grass grew.

The ostrich, the gazelle, the giraffe, the monkey, the rabbit, the tortoise, the zebra, and all the other animals were hungry. They searched in the jungle, they searched by the river, they searched on the great flat plain, but they could find nothing to eat.

At last all the animals gathered together and they said, "Let us go together across the great flat plain until we come to something we can eat."

And so all the animals, except for the lion, who was king and lived in the jungle, walked across the flat, empty land. They walked and walked. After many days, they saw a small bump on the edge of the flat land.

Then they saw that the small bump was a tree.

And the tree was very tall.

And the tree had fruit on it, such fruit as they had never seen before.

It was as red as pomegranates, as yellow as bananas, as green as melons, as purple as plums, as orange as mangos, and it smelled like all the fruits of the world.

But the tree was so tall and the branches so high that even the giraffe couldn't reach the fruit. And the trunk was so smooth that even the monkey couldn't climb the tree.

The animals sat on the ground and cried because the fruit smelled so good and they were so hungry.

At last, when they were too tired to cry any longer, a very old tortoise spoke.

"O animals," she said, "my great-great-great-grandmother told me a story about a wonderful tree. The fruit of that tree was delicious and good to eat. But it could be reached only by those who knew the name of the tree."

The animals cried out, "But who can tell us the name of the tree?"

The very old tortoise answered, "The king knows. We must send someone to ask him."

"I will go," said the gazelle. "I am the fastest runner of us all." And that was true.

So the gazelle started out across the great flat plain. He ran like an arrow shot from a bow, and as he ran he thought, "How lucky the animals are that I am willing to go to the king. No one can run as fast as I."

Indeed, it was not long before the gazelle reached the jungle and the place by the river where the king lived.

The king was sitting with his tail neatly wrapped around him. Every hair in his golden coat lay smooth and shining. He spoke kindly to the gazelle. "What do you wish of me," he said.

"O great king," said the gazelle, "all the animals are hungry and we have found a tree filled with wonderful fruit. But we cannot eat the fruit until we know the name of the tree."

"I will tell you," said the lion, "but you must remember, for I don't want to have to tell anyone else. The name of the tree is Ungalli."

"Ungalli," said the gazelle. "I will run as fast as the wind and I will reach the tree before I can possibly forget."

The gazelle thanked the king and began to run through the jungle and across the great flat plain. He thought about how happy all the animals would be, and how they would thank him and be grateful to him. He thought about this so hard that he did not see a rabbit hole that lay in his path, not far from where the animals were waiting. He stepped in it and went head over hoofs over head over hoofs. He landed in a heap at the foot of the tree.

"What is the name of the tree?" shouted the animals.

The gazelle shook his head. He shook it again. But the name was gone. "I can't remember," he whispered.

The animals groaned. "We will have to send someone else," they said. "Someone who will not forget."

"I will go," said the elephant. "I never forget anything."

The animals nodded, for this was true. And so the elephant strode off across the great flat plain.

"I will not forget," she said to herself. "I can remember anything I choose to. Even the names of all my cousins." The elephant had hundreds of cousins. "Or the names of all the stars in the sky."

When the elephant arrived at the edge of the river, the king was sitting in his usual place, but the end of his tail was twitching and his fur was ruffled.

"What do you want," he growled.

"O king," said the elephant, "all the animals are hungry . . ."

"I know," said the lion, "and you want to know the name of the tree with the wonderful fruit. I will tell you, but don't you forget because I absolutely will not tell anyone else. The name of the tree is Ungalli."

"I will not forget," said the elephant haughtily. "I never forget anything." And she turned and began to make her way out of the jungle.

"Forget," she grumbled to herself. "Me, forget! Why, I can remember the names of all the trees in this jungle." And she began to name them. When she had finished the jungle trees,

she went on to all the other trees in Africa. She was just starting on the trees of the rest of the world when she happened to step in the very rabbit hole that had tripped the gazelle. Her foot fitted exactly into the hole, so exactly that she couldn't get it out.

The animals waiting under the tree saw the elephant and ran toward her calling, "What is the name of the tree?"

The elephant pulled and tugged and pulled and tugged, and at last with a great *pop* her foot came out of the hole.

"I can't remember," she said crossly, "and I don't care. That tree has caused far too much trouble already."

The animals didn't even groan. They were too tired and too hungry.

After a long time a very young tortoise spoke.

"O animals," he said, "I will go and find out the name of the tree."

"You!" said the animals. "But you are so young and you are so small and you are so slow."

"Yes," said the very young tortoise. "But I know how to remember. I learned from my great-great-great-grandmother, the one who told you about the tree."

The animals had nothing to say. And the little tortoise was already on his way. It is true that he was slow. But by putting one short leg ahead of the other he crossed the great flat plain, went through the jungle, and arrived at the place by the river where the king lived.

The king was not sitting in his usual place. He was pacing up and down the bank of the river, waving his tail. His fur was standing on end.

When he saw the very young tortoise, he roared, "If you have come to ask me the name of the tree, go home. I have told the gazelle and I have told the elephant that the name of the tree is Ungalli, and I will *not* tell you."

The very young tortoise nodded his head politely. He turned and began to walk out of the jungle.

As he walked he said, "Ungalli, Ungalli, the name of the tree is Ungalli. Ungalli, Ungalli, the name of the tree is Ungalli."

And he went on saying it as he crossed the great flat plain. "Ungalli, Ungalli, the name of the tree is Ungalli."

And he never stopped saying it, even when he got tired, even when he got thirsty. Because that is what his great-great-great-grandmother had told him to do. Even when he fell right to the bottom of that same rabbit hole, the very young tortoise just climbed out saying, "Ungalli, Ungalli, the name of the tree is Ungalli."

None of the animals saw him coming. They were sitting under the tree, looking at the ground. The very young tortoise walked straight up to the foot of the tree and said in a loud voice, "The name of the tree is Ungalli!"

The animals looked up.

They saw the branches of the tree bend down so low that they could reach the wonderful fruit that was as red as pomegranates, as yellow as bananas, as green as melons, as purple as plums, and as orange as mangos, and smelled like all the fruits of the world.

The animals ate. They ate until they could eat no more. And then they lifted the very young tortoise high in the air and marched around the tree chanting, "Ungalli, Ungalli, the name of the tree is Ungalli," because they did not want to forget. And they never did.

MARGARET H. LIPPERT is a professional storyteller who comes from a family of Irish storytellers. A classroom teacher for many years, she taught children's literature and storytelling at Bank Street College of Education and at Teachers College, Columbia University, where she earned her doctorate. She has lived and taught in Tanzania, East Africa, and in Guatemala, Central America. She now lives in the Cascade Mountains in Washington State with her husband and two daughters.

𝒜UTHORS AND STORYTELLERS

Aesop, credited with the original telling of "The Ant and the Grasshopper" and "The Boy Who Cried Wolf," as well as many other fables, was a Greek slave who lived about 600 B.C. For many years, Aesop's fables were handed down orally from generation to generation. No one knows how many of the stories attributed to Aesop were actually composed by him.

Baylor, Byrd, who collected "The Maze" from a Pima student, Christine Manuel, in Arizona, is a prolific writer and storyteller. Some of her other books include *When Clay Sings*, *The Desert Is Theirs*, and *Hawk, I'm Your Brother*.

Belpré, Pura (1889-1982), teller of "The Shepherd and the Princess," was born in Puerto Rico. She later moved to New York City, where she worked as a librarian and told stories to children. When she looked for folk tales from Puerto Rico to read to them, she couldn't find any, so she began to write down folk tales she had heard as a child. Some of her books are *Ote: A Puerto Rican Folk Tale*, *The Dance of the Animals*, and *Once in Puerto Rico*.

Bruchac, Joseph, teller of "How Grandmother Spider Stole the Sun," is a poet, novelist, and storyteller. Born in the Adirondacks, Bruchac draws on the legends and myths of those mountains as well as on his own Native American (Abenaki) ancestry. He and Michael J. Caduto are coauthors of the book *Keepers of the Earth*, from which this selection was taken. They also wrote *Keepers of the Animals*.

Bryan, Ashley, teller of "Jackal's Favorite Game," was born in New York City. His parents came from the island of Antigua. He was formerly a professor at Dartmouth College. Bryan now has a studio on Little Cranberry Island in Maine. He has written, compiled, and illustrated many books, including *The Ox of the Wonderful Horns and Other African Folktales*; *Beat the Story Drum, Pum-Pum*; and *The Cat's Purr*.

111

Carroll, Lewis (1832-1898), author of "The Walrus and the Carpenter," was born Charles L. Dodgson. He wrote *Alice's Adventures in Wonderland; Jabberwocky; Through the Looking-Glass and What Alice Found There;* and numerous poems.

Climo, Shirley, is the author of "Spider's Friends and Foes" and "Father Spider Comes to Dinner." Born in 1928, she has written several books including *The Cobweb Christmas; Gopher, Tanker, and the Admiral;* and *Someone Saw a Spider: Spider Facts and Folktales.*

Floating Eaglefeather (1953-1991), teller of "Why the Baby Says, 'Goo-Goo'," was a traveling bard. He traveled around the world every two years, telling stories and learning new ones as he went.

Harper, Wilhelmina (1884-1973), teller of "The Gunniwolf," edited numerous anthologies of stories for young people, including *Dog Show, A Selection of Favorite Dog Stories; Flying Hoofs: Stories of Horses;* and *For Love of Country: Stories of Young Patriots.*

Hayes, Joe, author of "Frog and Locust" and "Some Great Bait," has based many of his stories on tales from the varied cultures of New Mexico. His books include *The Day It Snowed Tortillas* and *The Checker-Playing Hound Dog.*

Jackson, Ken (Grey Eagle), teller of the tale "How Wolf Helped the Sami," teaches communications and American Indian studies at the University of Washington. His Scandinavian heritage is reflected in the Sami stories he collects in Samiland, formerly Lapland; his Ojibwe heritage is honored in the book of Raven stories he wrote, which is being published in Norway.

Lipman, Doug, teller of "The Tailor," travels nationwide telling stories and teaching storytelling workshops. His audiocassettes of stories include "Folktales of Strong Women" and "Tell It With Me," a Parents Choice Award Winner. He lives in Massachusetts.

Lottridge, Celia Barker, who wrote "The Name of the Tree," is a founding member of the Storytellers' School of Toronto. Her books include *The Juggler* and *One Watermelon Seed.*

MacDonald, Margaret Read, author of "Udala Tree" and "The Little Rooster and the Turkish Sultan," is a professional storyteller, children's librarian, and author. She wrote *The Storyteller's Sourcebook* and many books of stories including *Twenty Tellable Tales, Look Back and See,* and *Peace Tales.*

Manuel, Christine, teller of "The Maze," was a student at St. John's School in Laveen, Arizona, when she told the story to Byrd Baylor. Baylor published the story in her collection entitled *And It Is Still That Way: Legends told by Arizona Indian Children with notes by Byrd Baylor*. Manuel is Pima and the story is from her heritage.

McCormick, Dell J. (1892-1949), teller of "When the Rain Came Up from China," also wrote *Paul Bunyan Swings His Axe* and *Tall Timber Tales: More Paul Bunyan Stories*. In 1940 he received the Pacific Northwest Library Association Young Readers' Choice Award for *Paul Bunyan Swings His Axe*.

Morton, Richard, composer of "One Man's Trash," is a songwriter and performer. He recorded this song on an audiocassette by the same title.

Ross, Gayle, grew up in Texas. She remembers listening to the stories and songs shared by her Cherokee grandmother. Ross travels throughout the United States telling stories both alone and in tandem with Texas storyteller Elizabeth Ellis. The Cherokee legend "Strawberries" is one of Ross's favorite stories.

Schimmel, Nancy, author of "The Rainhat," is a professional storyteller from California. "The Rainhat" is from her storytelling classic *Just Enough to Make a Story*.

Uchida, Yoshiko, is the teller of "The Tubmaker Who Flew to the Sky," from her collection of Japanese folk tales entitled *The Magic Listening Cap*. In 1972 she won the Silver Medal for Best Juvenile Book by a California Author from the Commonwealth Club of California for *Samurai of Gold Hill*. In addition to several collections of Japanese folk tales, she has also written *The Birthday Visitor*, *The Full Circle*, and *A Jar of Dreams*.

White, E. B. (1899-1985), was the author of *Charlotte's Web*, a 1953 Newbery Honor Book. White coauthored *The Elements of Style* with William Strunk, Jr. White's style and humor were important in distinguishing *The New Yorker's* first thirty years. His other books include *Stuart Little* and *The Trumpet of the Swan*.

Wolkstein, Diane, author of *The Cool Ride in the Sky*, is a professional storyteller who lives in New York and travels internationally telling stories and giving storytelling workshops. She has written many other award-winning folk tales, including *The Magic Orange Tree and Other Haitian Folktales*, *The Red Lion*, and *The Banza*, a Reading Rainbow Selection. Her audiocassettes of stories include "Romping" and "Hans Christian Andersen in Central Park," both Parents' Choice Gold Seal Award winners.

113

INDEX

INDEX OF LITERATURE BY ORIGIN

$\mathcal{A}$UTHOR AND STORYTELLER INDEX

Index of Titles

TEACHER'S READ ALOUD NOTES

TEACHER'S READ ALOUD NOTES

TEACHER'S READ ALOUD NOTES